THE TEN MOST EFFECTIVE SELF-CARE HEALING TECHNIQUES

What You Can Do to Maximize Your Healing Journey

D1267772

The Spiritual Strengths Healing Plan

Richard P. Johnson, Ph.D.

ISBN 978-0-9895130-6-7

10 9 8 7 6 5 4 3 2 1

First Edition

Cover design by Megan Irwin

Edited by Maggie Singleton

Printed in the United States of America

BOOKS IN THE SPIRITUAL STRENGTHS HEALING SERIES

by Richard P. Johnson

- God Give Me Strength! Finding the Inner Power to Turn Your Illness/Brokenness/Life Transition Around

- Discover Your Spiritual Strengths: Find Health, Healing, and Happiness (flagship book of the Spiritual Strengths Healing Plan)

- Body, Mind, Spirit: Tapping the Healing Power Within

- Prayers for Spiritual Strength: Physical Illnesses, Emotional Broken Places, and/or Spiritual Dis-eases

- The Ten Most Effective Self-Care Healing Techniques: What You Can Do to Maximize Your Healing Journey

- The Power of Smiling: Using Positive Psychology for Optimal Health & Healing

- Healing Wisdom: 101 Spiritual Truths for Healing Your Illness

- Healing and Depression: Finding Peace in the Midst of Transition, Turmoil, or Illness

- Staying Spiritually Centered for Optimal Healing: Even When You're Sick or Life Seems Out of Control

- Seeking Significance: How to Discover New Self-Direction and New Life-Purpose Beyond Your (Unwanted) Life Transition

Caregiving Titles

- Caregiving from Your Spiritual Strengths: The Ten Fundamental Principles for Optimal Success

- Because I Care...Inspiration for Caregiving for Spouses, Health Care Personnel, Family & Friends

The Spiritual Strengths Healing Plan

The Spiritual Strengths Healing Plan allows you to harness your internal healing power! It is not "faith healing" in which one relies on divine intervention as the sole means for physical cure, nor does it promise cure. Its purpose is healing and is best seen as a supplement to and support for current medical practices. The Spiritual Strengths Healing Plan's philosophy holds that each individual needs to seek the best and most appropriate medical and psychological care they can, in accord with their own personal wishes, and supplement their care with this Plan.

Please note that you will see the word "illness" throughout this book in its broadest sense and may indicate any (or a combination) of the following:

I. Physical Sicknesses

Cancer, heart disease, MS, Lupus, migraine, addictions, hypochondriasis, pain, weight management/loss, smoking cessation, pneumonia, COPD, hypertension, arthritis, immune disorders, Parkinson's, diabetes, stroke, chronic fatigue etc., etc.

II. Psychological Issues

Anxiety, depression, personality disorders, OCD, manipulation, stress, bi-polar disorder, etc., etc.

III. Emotional Issues

Being unrealistic, lacking responsibility, low-self-esteem, career focus issues, poor organization skills, family disharmony, anger management, fears, perfectionism, marriage discontent, lifelessness, infidelity, irritability, chronic lateness, caregiving, etc., etc.

IV. Spiritual Dis-eases

Peace of mind and heart, un-forgiveness, existential angst, inner pain, grudges, scrupulosity, incomplete developmental transitions, guilt, grief and unresolved grief, regrets, blame, disappointments, so-called "unfinished business," resentments, etc., etc.

V. Spiritual Direction & Growth

Gaining better clarity of God's plan in your life, and breaking through barriers that may be hindering your faith journey.

Where do <u>you</u> need healing?

For more information about the Spiritual Strengths Healing Plan, log on to...

<u>www.SpiritualStrengthsHealing.com</u>

The Spiritual Strengths Healing Institute

Learning the art of healing for self and others

Contents

Contents... 9

Introduction 11

Self-Care Technique One: Education for Healing 17

Self-Care Technique Two: Healing Relaxation and Meditation 19

Self-Care Technique Three: Healing Prayer................................ 29

Self-Care Technique Four: Imagination and Guided Imagery 45

Self-Care Technique Five: The Healing Value of Smiling............... 57

Self-Care Technique Six: Healing Art and Drawing...................... 65

Self-Care Technique Seven: Life Review and Spiritual
    Autobiography.. 71

Self-Care Technique Eight: Personality Voice Awareness 83

Self-Care Technique Nine: Healing Circles 91

Self-Care Technique Ten: Praying the Labyrinth 97

End Note 107

Introduction

The advent of illness, with all its potential diminishment (even if it's temporary), emotional turmoil, psychological insult, and spiritual challenges all present trauma to anyone's life. Grave, chronic, and especially terminal conditions confound your life and alter your image of the world, yourself, and God.

Even in the best of situations, in which sufficient family support, adequate financial resources, the availability of good caregivers, and the presence of an intact self-esteem are all "in place," you can still stumble and falter emotionally. When these ideal conditions are not present, psychic disturbances and mental distress can emerge, causing even greater turmoil.

The Spiritual Strengths Healing Plan is built on the simple belief that healing (as distinct from curing) is not of this world and that a keen awareness of God's presence within is essential, regardless of your physical condition.

The restorative power of God is an awesome force for healing that lies within each of us. Fortunately, various techniques are available to help stimulate it.

Current research has clearly demonstrated that persons can mobilize the energies of their inner forces of healing to bring increased integrity and wholeness to their entire illness experience regardless of its type. This book teaches 10 ways to take stronger charge of your spiritual strengths and focus them on your illness, whatever it may be.

I've assembled these 10 healing techniques quite intentionally for The Spiritual Strengths Healing Plan. I've taken some of these 10 from research that documents the restorative and healing characteristics of the techniques listed here. Others I've taken from my own clinical experience and have applied them to the illness experience—whether that is as a patient or as a caregiver. I call these the ten "most effective" techniques because I've seen them work best, both for me as a illness survivor and for my counseling patients seeking ways to shift their illness experience from a "reign of terror" to a time of promise. The ten techniques include—

1. **Education for Healing**: Discovering God's unique healing power within you.

2. **Healing Relaxation and Meditation**: Centering on your healing strengths.

3. **Healing Prayer**: Connecting with the Divine Healer.

4. **Imagination and Guided Imagery**: Spring-boarding to new healing.

5. **The Healing Value of Smiling**: Changing your mood for maximum healing.

6. **Healing Art & Drawings**: Discovering new dimensions of healing.

7. **Life Review & Spiritual Autobiography**: Finding God's healing hand throughout your life.

8. **Personality Voice Awareness**: Discovering healing whispers within you.

9. **Healing Circles**: Feeling healing strengths from others.

10. **Praying the Labyrinth**: Learning a new Healing pathway.

These ten techniques are a solid and reliable means of helping you and/or others tap into the healing power within. This list is not exhaustive. There are many other techniques, but these ten can be used with confidence. I recommend that you keep a journal of your spiritual thoughts and feelings during your illness journey, which can serve as your spiritual/healing growth treasury.

Helplessness

Rigorous research has determined that the mental and emotional condition of helplessness—the behavioral consequence of deep discouragement—is a particularly noxious condition for anyone dealing with illness. During the Korean conflict the term "brainwashed" was used to describe the puzzling reaction some American prisoners of war (POWs) exhibited in confinement. With no physical torture at all some POWS would react in a passive, even docile manner. At the end of the conflict American psychologists determined that the Korean captors had devised ways to render the POWs completely helpless. In such a psychologically-disoriented state, they lost their will to live, all sense of hope, and feelings of life—they became discouraged, lifeless, and eventually helpless.

Medical personnel notice much the same in patients who react poorly to their illness by becoming lifeless. Recent illness research investigating this phenomenon generates new understanding that helplessness has very dangerous physical effects on your neurochemistry. Helplessness is dramatically stressful to the body—releasing the stress hormones adrenalin and cortisol. This hormonal surge in turn undermines your immune system—making it dramatically less robust in its ongoing fight against all bodily attacks of illness. Just as helplessness made servicemen less effective, medical remedies are made less effective when patients feel helpless—as if they can do nothing.

Illness, much like an advancing army, will overtake you if you don't enlist your vital healing powers (your spiritual strengths) to stand strong against the onslaught. God has given you what you need to keep your mood buoyant, your motivation spirited, and your defenses strong. The techniques in this book will help draw these defenses out.

When you combine your six premier spiritual strengths with the 10 "spiritual weapons" described in this book, you will have created a bulwark that is impenetrable to illness and any feelings of helplessness.

If you haven't yet taken the **Spiritual Strengths Healing Profile** (SSHP), I encourage you to do so now. Recognizing your six most potent spiritual strengths will greatly enhance the application of these 10 techniques as well as lead you to a greater appreciation for the strengths God has entrusted to you. Go to www.spiritualstrengthshealing.com and follow the easy directions you will find there. You'll be invited to respond to 120 statements as they apply to you. The 20-page document you'll receive will provide you invaluable insight into your personality and God-given strengths.

A Final Note: I am a Christian by birth and practice, and I have no doubt that this lifetime faith walk shows through in these pages. Please don't infer from this bias that this book is only for Christians. I believe that the truths in these pages are universal. I've written them from a Christian perspective because it's the only one that is natural for me. If you are not a Christian, then I ask you to filter my bias so that my words ring clear and true to you. I thank you.

I wish you God's love, nurturing peace, and sustaining strength throughout your illness journey.

Richard P. Johnson, Ph.D.

Your Spiritual Personality

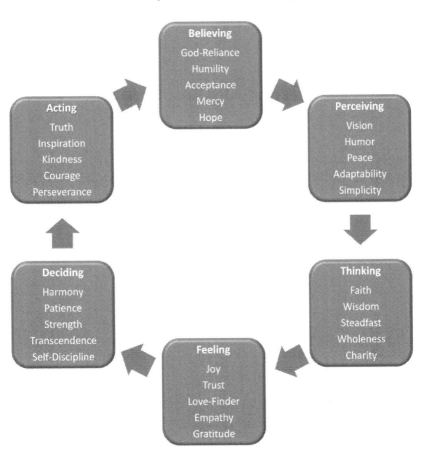

Believing
God-Reliance
Humility
Acceptance
Mercy
Hope

Acting
Truth
Inspiration
Kindness
Courage
Perseverance

Perceiving
Vision
Humor
Peace
Adaptability
Simplicity

Deciding
Harmony
Patience
Strength
Transcendence
Self-Discipline

Thinking
Faith
Wisdom
Steadfast
Wholeness
Charity

Feeling
Joy
Trust
Love-Finder
Empathy
Gratitude

Self-Care Technique One

Education for Healing

Everyone has heard that knowledge is power...knowledge about healing is no exception. We need to educate ourselves in the processes and procedures of healing, and The Spiritual Strengths Healing Plan provides a comprehensive educational program for you to learn the power of healing and apply its principles to energize your illness journey.

The first educational "gem" of The Spiritual Strengths Healing Plan is its' new conception of personality. Healing calls you to be a good steward of your personality, not a slave to it.

Your personality operates by performing the following six functions (as depicted in the diagram on page 15):

- Believing
- Perceiving
- Thinking
- Feeling
- Deciding
- Acting

Together these functions form the full range of psychological processes that allow you to travel the path toward greater personal power, enhanced self-esteem, better interpersonal relations, improved health, and integrating wholeness. But these six alone would prove insufficient for the task of healing without the cornerstone—God. Without God, we can experience no genuine healing. You might want to consult Part I of the flagship book, Discover Your Spiritual Strengths, for a more in-depth discussion of your personality and how it works best.

The second educational tool for healing introduced in The Spiritual Strengths Healing Plan is the thirty Spiritual Strengths. Spiritual Strengths are pieces of God-given healing power on the earthly plane. Spiritual Strengths give you goals to follow, ideals to stretch toward, and targets to shoot for. The Spiritual Strengths model gives you the framework of healing and the thirty healing virtues flesh it out to create a fully formed whole. For more on this fascinating and spiritually-practical understanding of your personality strengths, consult chapters 6, 8, 10, 12, 14, and 16 of Discover Your Spiritual Strengths.

The Spiritual Strengths Healing Plan provides a powerful educational foundation, a unified curriculum of healing as well as a spiritual development that can guide you faithfully along the healing path. It gives you structure and support. It provides a road map as well as a vehicle. It gives you all the equipment you need to travel the highway of healing and arrive safe and whole at your destination.

Self-Care Technique Two

Healing Relaxation and Meditation

To say that illness is stressful for the patient and the caregiver would be a gross understatement. Relaxation in all forms then is a requirement not a luxury for anyone journeying with illness...relaxation then is essential for healing. Your body, mind, and spirit need time and space to marshal vital healing forces and focus them on healing. You need relaxation to regroup and refocus, renew and restore, recoup and revitalize. Relaxation balances you.

Physiologically, relaxation means a reduction in nervous system stimulation that blocks or prevents the flight-or fight stress response. One of the pioneer proponents of relaxation is Dr. Herbert Benson or Harvard University. In his book <u>The Relaxation Revolution</u> released in 2010, you can read about all of the powerful effects relaxation has upon your health. Most exciting for those challenged with cancer are recent findings about replacing tumor-creating genes with immune-enhancing genes by simple relaxation!

Benson and his colleagues have worked for over 40 years on the notion that relaxation is powerful medicine. Even small steps toward intentional relaxation can produce measurable benefits. Relaxing 15 to 20 minutes once, or better yet, twice a day, can lower levels of adrenaline and cortisol as well as decrease blood pressure, heart rate, and respiration. Perhaps even more important for patients is how relaxation enhances immune functioning and balances the activity in the right and left hemispheres of the brain.

Relaxation, practiced in almost any form, produces therapeutic effects. The benefits of relaxation in the treatment of just about every known physical and emotional malady have been thoroughly documented. Relaxation is an almost foolproof procedure that pays handsome dividends. Relaxation, quieting the body and mind is the first step toward accessing your inner teacher by allowing you to focus within yourself, thereby shutting out the hectic, frantic, and judgmental world. Here is the starting point toward peace. The road toward spiritual and emotional solace begins through a gate called relaxation.

Prevention

Preventive relaxation strategies include asking for help, exercising, light reading, soothing music, massage, and one that's commonly overlooked—the ability to say "no!" Illness changes you; it certainly can deplete your stamina. Finding your "new normal" is always a guessing game. Healing means you can't use yesterday's energy to address today's stress; you need to reassess "where you are" today and make adjustments in what you can and can't (shouldn't) do. All of these can refresh and renew you so you can "fill the tank" and continue on your illness journey.

Intervention: Deep Breathing

Beyond prevention of distress, you can look to relaxation techniques for help—and there is ample help available—to relieve an already stressful condition. One relaxation technique you can use anytime and anywhere is deep breathing. As you become more distressed, you tend to take only half breaths. Such shallow breathing reduces blood flow and in itself signals the body that all is not well. Deep breathing does the opposite—it enhances blood flow and activates a healing spark within you. Go ahead and try it right now...

1. Slowly begin taking deeper breaths. Slowly draw in air through your nose and intentionally bring it all the way down to your belly.

2. Fill your belly with air, then inflate your entire rib cage with the air, and follow that in sequence by expanding your chest with air. This is called a 3-part abdominal breath.

3. Now hold it for a few second before slowly exhaling—beginning with your chest, then your rib cage, and finally your belly.

4. Now, wait a second or two before you inhale again or until your feel that urge to take in a breath. This urge is your life force, the energy in you that craves life that urges you to move on. This "spark" comes from your center and is animated (given life) by your spiritual strengths.

You can train yourself to breathe this way anytime and anywhere you find yourself, in whatever position, and in any frame of mind. Even very short "sessions" of two or three minutes bring you a renewal of spirit, a calmness of heart, and a more peaceful soul.

Deep Muscle Relaxation

The next step toward deeper relaxation is to focus on your muscles. The standard method is called deep muscle relaxation where you assume a comfortable position (usually lying down) and sequentially go through all your muscles—gradually tightening and then releasing each one at a time. You can start with your head and work your way down to your toes, or you can do the opposite. Tighten the "focus" muscle on your inhale, and loosen it as you exhale. Once you proceed through your entire body, retreat into a calmness that innervates you with pleasant warmth and serenity of mind. Remain in this relaxed "space" as long as you'd like, all the while letting your thoughts and feelings simply come and go—taking little or no notice of their content or emotion.

Exercise

Exercise is a natural relaxant and a most helpful adjunct to your daily routine. Any kind of body movement can be exercise, but it's probably best to choose exercise that is pleasurable, or at least non-offensive, if only to help you stay motivated. A gentle walk is great or perhaps some time on an exercise machine; stretching is also an excellent exercise in itself. Exercise helps you relax in two ways: 1) it squeezes out any toxins that have accumulated in your body, and 2) it helps activate neurochemicals that give you a sense of well-being. It's important to start slowly and never, never overdo. Exercise mobilizes health-enhancing endorphins while it flushes out health-diminishing adrenalin and cortisol.

Quiet Time, Silence & Stillness

Any techniques or activities that help you "live in the holy now" will certainly bring you to a new level of relaxation: listening to soothing music, "tuning in" to your inner wisdom, taking a calming bath, enjoying a satisfying cup of tea, chatting with a good friend or confidante, or reading a good book all serve to calm your body, mind, heart, and soul.

Throughout your day, focus on your movement. For example, as you walk down a hallway, become aware of how the soles of your feet feel as they touch the floor. Take notice as you peel an orange—genuinely appreciating the wonder and miracle of the orange. Focus on all your activities in similar ways. Find yourself being very deliberate in your actions from eating food to brushing your teeth, from drinking water to noticing the color of the sky.

Try to lessen stimulation that in any way disturbs you and replace it with a grateful heart—this alone is marvelously relaxing.

When your body is battling illness, you need time for rest. Distractions and entertainment, while pleasurable, are not necessarily restful. They may actually over-stimulate you and consequently invade your natural healing systems. For instance, watching TV is actually anything but restful. Although your body is stationary, your mind and other systems are racing. Solving a murder mystery, watching a football game, and especially watching the news can be stressful; none of this is true rest. True rest is when we create the appropriate environment that allows your entire being to recover, rebuild, and replenish. Your physical body is reclined, your breath moves fully and softly, your mind slows, your emotions ease, and a sense of peace and well-being envelops you when you are actually resting.

The Spiritual Strengths Illness Care Relaxation Method

I use the following relaxation method with my counseling patients. I find it brings about a general feeling of personal buoyancy and a more spiritually centered receptivity to God's healing power. This method works, and with regular practice, you will get better and better at it. Some people even report that the sensations of relaxation and peace they feel can actually become part of their "new normal" of being as they continue their illness journey. It works very well for both illness patients and illness caregivers.

The Spiritual Strengths Healing Relaxation Sequence

1. Wherever you are, arrange your body, clothing, and posture so you are maximally comfortable.

2. Imagine a point of light on the very top of your head; this point of light is God's healing power.

3. Imagine this point of light growing larger and larger until it covers your entire scalp—then your entire face. Mentally relax all the muscles laminated by this expanding light.

4. Imagine the muscles in the back of your neck. In your mind's eye "see" these neck muscles on either side of your vertebrae as made up of thousands of tiny muscle fibers that look like small rubber bands that are stretched tight and taut. Notice that as these rubber band muscle fibers begin to relax, they release extremely tiny droplets of what looks like black ink. This "black bile" is stress. Once this stress is released, it begins draining down your neck, your back, and right out of you.

5. Imagine the light of God's grace slowly covering your entire body and releasing the "black bile" throughout your body.

Meditation

Once physical relaxation has been sufficiently achieved, you can begin to quiet your mind through meditation. Meditation is as natural as sleeping, although it is quite different. In meditation, you are seeking a sharpened awareness; you journey deep within your mind to concentrate gently on a single, simple, even profound idea or concept. The process can move you to heightened understanding of yourself and a deepened faith in God found nowhere else. Again, meditation can be learned through many paths, all of which are constructed to bring peace and calm to a frenetic, chaotic, confused mind. The goal of meditation is to bring order, focus, structure, and above all, quiet to your entire personality.

The particular form of meditation that has "caught on" in illness treatment circles is called "mindfulness meditation" The method was devised by Jon Kabat-Zinn in his book Full Catastrophe Living.

Like all meditation, mindfulness meditation requires that you first enter into a relaxed state (which can be reached by using the Spiritual Strengths Illness Care method of relaxation mentioned above).

Once you become relaxed, mindfulness meditation asks that you simply allow any thoughts and any feelings to slide in and slide right out of your mind. Try not to capture the thought, try not to concentrate or entertain the thought or feeling...simply be a passive observer of them, almost a disinterested bystander who is detached from any personal involvement in the thought or feeling. Let the thought emerge, "see" it for what it is, only a thought and nothing more, and then let it fade away from any consciousness. You are mindful of the thought or feeling, but you have absolutely no need or desire to involve yourself in it—you view it as though you would view a leaf falling from a tree—an event of little personal involvement or consequence. Practicing mindfulness meditation helps you empty your mind of any "clutter" and cleanse your heart of any disturbing and diminishing emotions. You try to release any internal compulsion you may feel to address the thought or feeling—you remain free, unattached, and unaffected.

Two other forms of meditation include one-pointed and two-pointed meditation. In one-pointed meditation, you focus on one word (of your choosing) and remain focused on it for 15 to 20 minutes—repeating it ever so slowly over and over. Try to calibrate your internal recitation of the word with your breathing in any way that feels comfortable for you. You can choose any word or even a nonsense word that may carry meaning for you alone. Some common words are: peace, love, healing, light, grace, and gratitude. If your mind wanders away from the word, gently bring your attention back to the word very compassionately and with a gentle guiding hand of peace.

In two-pointed meditation, you focus on your breath as you practice mindfulness meditation described above. Other forms of meditation are Transcendental Meditation (TM), and Silva Mind Control, developed my Jose Silva.

The Spiritual Strengths Meditation Method

The Spiritual Strengths Healing Plan has developed two forms of meditation, both of which focus on your six spiritual strengths.

The first form is an advancement of mindfulness meditation, which I simply call Spiritual Strengths Mindfulness Meditation. It's accomplished in two steps that are really very simple; they go like this...

Drop into a relaxed state by using The Spiritual Strengths Healing Relaxation Sequence.

Become aware of any beliefs, perceptions, thoughts, feelings, decisions, or mental actions that emerge from your personality functions. As these beliefs, perceptions, thoughts, feelings, choices, or potential actions emerge from your personality functions, internally nod to them, and then just let them return back to their source again. You might bless each one as it arises from and recedes back into your personality "soup" by mentally placing a point of light of grace upon it. Blessing it doesn't mean you agree or disagree with the thought or feeling, etc.; you don't want to involve yourself in any one of them on an evaluative level. Just let them all "be"—there are no rights or wrongs, no need to even look twice. Don't worry if you can't discern whether it is a belief, a perception, a thought, a feeling, etc., at this point your simple recognition and blessing is all that matters. And please don't try to push the process by generating more personality activity; remember that your goal is to generate less not more activity.

The second The Spiritual Strengths Mindfulness Meditation method is equally simple but maximally effective.

1. Become as relaxed as you can.

2. Imagine yourself descending a long spiral staircase that leads, after many, many steps, into a beautiful chapel in your soul.

3. Reverently walk down the center isle of the chapel and sit in a chair you find there just inside the altar rail.

4. There you wait and pray, until you become aware that someone is with you.

5. You suddenly realize that this someone is Jesus.

6. He sits down next to you in a chair that simply materializes for him as he sits.

7. You tell him about your need for healing; you are very explicit about what you believe you need.

8. You listen intently to what Jesus says to you, and commit to incorporating this counsel into your life.

9. Remain in this meditative state with Jesus for as long as you wish before Jesus leaves you.

10. You then retrace your steps out of the chapel, and back up the steps to full conscious awareness.

Both of these meditation sequences offer a very practical and convenient means of accessing your spiritual strengths for Healing. Learn them, practice them, and make them an integral part of your personal healing plan.

Self-Care Technique Three

Healing Prayer

Prayer is your primary healing tool. Prayer, the spiritual action you take to bring you into connection with God, is an essential component in the Spiritual Strengths Healing Plan. Prayer provides you a road that leads to healing; it melts barriers that may be separating you from God. Prayer manifests the warmth of the unique and singular love that lies at the heart of your holy relationship with God's healing presence. Prayer is your conversation with God. There are many, many prayer forms but only one goal—communion with God.

The function of prayer is to become to the utmost what we are meant to be no matter what situation we are in.

The following are quotes from Sr. Joan Chittister's book, <u>Breath of the Soul</u>, a little prayer manual that I would heartily recommend to anyone connected with illness in any way.

- Prayer is the filter through which we begin to see all reality, all life, all decisions, all purposes, and all goals (page 70).

- Prayer tells us that there is more to life than what life shows us on the surface of it (page 71).

- Are we people of prayer or simply people who pray? (page 72).

- Prayer opens us to ourselves (page 74).

- God is not a vending machine (page 76).

- Prayer deepens our awareness (page 77).

- Private prayer is the only genuine path to real intimacy with God (page 80).

- The chaos inside us is the beginning of a relationship with God (page 84).

- Prayer helps us let go so that God can lead us and heal us (page 88).

- Prayer helps us learn the mind of God and the obstacles of our own heart (page 90).

- In prayer we are seeking the God who is seeking us (page 91).

- Prayer helps us listen to the voice within us calling us to seek more than we are ourselves alone   (page 97).

- The presence of absence is not the absence of presence (page 93).

- Prayer allows us to discover the Presence within that we never knew before (page 100).

The Power of Prayer

Prayer can spell the difference between personal growth and stagnation, between energizing development and lifeless inertia, and between spiritual vibrancy and a shallow emptiness in your time with illness. Prayer is a mighty force constantly promoting individual self-control, personal happiness, and spiritual attainment. Prayer is your avenue to God's healing power unparalleled in the world, the path to a freedom and independence our worldly culture cannot provide. Prayer is your road to personal satisfaction, joy, and good cheer unknown on the material level. Because prayer is so important throughout your life, but especially so in your illness time, you owe it to yourself to come to a clear understanding of this communication with Divinity called prayer!

"Prayer is a fountain of joy and an immeasurable source of love. When we walk the way of prayer, we walk the way of conversion. We cannot have one without the other."

(Into the Heart of Faith, Fr. Dennis Billy, C.Ss.R., Liguori Publications, Liguori, MO 1999, page 60)

Your time with illness is full of potential "life work;" this holy time can be filled with spiritual growth and character enhancement. You are called to accomplish so much during this sacred time: integrate the wisdom of your years, lest you fall into personal confusion and character fragmentation; let go of pretense and uncover once again the source of wonder and beauty, lest you slip into anger and irritability; take stock of all the gifts you have received and used in your life, or risk descent into dependency and despondency; discover the creative completion in your life, or else face helplessness and infantilization, and others.

Your advancing spirituality is the theme that runs like a golden thread through all these developmental tasks of your illness journey. It is this thread which not only holds you together as you move through these years, but it is also this thread that gives your life its central purpose.

All of this and much, much more is waiting at your personal doorstep; will you address the "life work" of your illness time with vitality, with gusto, and with spiritual grit; or will you shrink from it and enter into a soul numbing monotony of a lackluster existence? By what force or energy can you mount this work and find the joy that resides therein?

What is Prayer?

Noted theologian, Karl Rahner, S.J., says that *"Prayer is a voice from the depth of the heart. Prayer is the language in which the heart asks God to hear it."* (Happiness Through Prayer, Newman Press, Westminister, Maryland, 1958, page 45). Prayer is your effort to approach God. Prayer does so many things for you.

Yet you must make the first move toward God in prayer. God does not coerce you in any way; you must be proactive in prayer. Prayer propels you up toward God like the outstretched wings of a bird catching a spiraling updraft. Prayer expands you, it broadens your perception and your understanding; prayer gives you insight.

Prayer is the gift of being able to put my life into the hands of God, and trust the path that opens before me. Whether I think I would have wanted it or not.

Prayer sustains you because it moves you toward your most noble parts and allows you to align yourself with the Spirit's plan for your life. Prayer inspires you and gives your life direction that you otherwise wouldn't have. Whatever else prayer does, when done in earnest; it expands your own communion with God. Prayer heightens your capacity for truly understanding your God-given gifts. Your capacity for receiving the grace of God is clearly connected with your prayer life. Prayer gives you a celestial pause so you can detach from the daily routines of life and find spiritual refreshment; it allows you to recharge your spiritual batteries.

Persons with illness are often pulled toward prayer even more during this time of personal chaos or turmoil, and yet your goal should be to pray unendingly, all the time, persistently. It is in your ongoing prayer throughout all the ups and downs of illness that gives you the most peace. Particularly in these times of crisis, you may find yourself praying as though you are trying to change the Mind of God; trying to somehow convince God that your solution to the problem is what God ought to adopt as well. Sometimes you can mistakenly use prayer as a means of enlisting God onto your side. Actually, prayer does exactly the opposite; the goal of prayer is to help change your mind toward God, toward God's children, toward yourself, and toward the circumstances of your life.

For prayer to become maximally effective in your life you must be persistent in your prayer. Regularly and continuously touching your own soul with the Divine increases your receptivity to God's power in your life.

We are to pray in everyday life, and we are to make everyday life our prayer.

Rahner, page 45

Prayer does not insure that you will be insulated from the trials and tribulations of your illness. Yet, prayer does offer you the spiritual potentials of strength, perseverance, and spiritual stamina so you may remain steadfast in faith and calm of demeanor regardless of your personal travails. Prayer is your stimulus to grow in the face of illness; prayer is not a means of avoiding the conflict. Prayer offers no escape hatch from your worldly duties and responsibilities during your time with illness. Prayer does offer a magnificent means for vigorously entering into the fray of illness, perhaps the most complicated human predicament and yet, at the same time, prayer offers you a calm detachment from the outcome of your illness.

Is All Prayer Answered?

God does respond to your prayer. However, the answer that you may want God to give may not in fact be the answer that God deems best for you. The answer to your prayer is determined entirely by God, all knowing and all loving, not by your own capricious whims and desires. When your prayer appears to remain unanswered, this apparent oversight by God may actually be a delay waiting for a time when a better, more comprehensive answer can be offered.

The answer to your prayer may simply remain "on deposit," as it were, waiting for that time when you have spiritually progressed to a point where you can appreciate the value of the answer you've been given. God's time is not your time. God answers prayer by giving truth; and sometimes you simply don't wish to know the truth or you can't grasp this piece of the grand spiritual truth that is embodied in God's response.

At other times your prayer seemingly goes unanswered because the true answer to your prayer is something that you simply could not understand at this time in your spiritual development. You may not yet be spiritually mature enough to constructively use the answer fruitfully. In some instances God indeed does give you an answer, but you haven't yet developed the spiritual "eyes" to see that your prayer may have already been answered.

It is entirely possible that when you reach your immortal status beyond this world, you shall then understand that on those occasions when you thought God was somehow deaf to your petitions and your desires, that in fact you did receive an answer, indeed <u>the</u> answer, and you simply didn't recognize it. All prayer is spiritual, and must be heard in this spiritual form first. When you ask God for things outside the realm of the spiritual, you may not recognize the spiritual answer that emerges.

You are God's child, and God is your spiritual parent. How many times are parents required to say "no" to their children? When children hear the answer "no" they sometimes act like they haven't heard the answer at all, because it wasn't the answer that they wanted. You are God's child, and sometimes when you make a request of God, the answer comes back, "no." Since you don't want to hear such a response, you overlook or otherwise dismiss the "no" answer and continue your prayer requests.

You can easily forget that "no" is a very clear answer. Parents surely don't say "yes" to each and every request made by their child. A "no" answer is given, not to hurt the child but actually for the good of the child. If the "no" response was withheld, the child grows without boundaries and never learns self-discipline. The child forever loses this character development and spirit-enhancing opportunity of learning why the "no" answer might have given him in that particular situation. Benevolent earthly parents act as reflections of God in heaven. Like an unruly child who has a tantrum when he doesn't "get his way," you too may have a spiritual tantrum when you believe that your prayers haven't been answered.

Another reason that you may think that God doesn't hear your prayer is because God's answer to you is in the form of an attitude adjustment. Attitudinal change, actually changing your mind about the situation you have prayed for, may go completely unnoticed. Your change in attitude may only become apparent to you when someone else, perhaps a confidante, inquires how you're doing regarding a life issue that previously "tied you in knots." When you respond something like, *'Oh, that doesn't bother me anymore.'* you are signaling how much your attitude has changed. Could this attitudinal change be God's answer to your prayer?

Types of Prayer

It is beyond the scope of this chapter to review all the various types of prayer; actually a case could be made that there are as many different forms and styles of prayer as there are persons praying. Some common types of prayer however bear mentioning:

- Petition: When you feel in need, you spontaneously reach for God to make your life better. *'God, give me _(strength)_.'*

- Thanksgiving: When you sense a stirring of dependency, prayer converts this sensation into gratitude and profound appreciation. *'God, you are so good to me.'*

- Supplication: When you feel distressed and powerless, you offer yourself to God, even bargain with God, if God will help; you will do such and such. *'God, please help me!'*

- Intercession: When you ask God to help others in some way. *'God, enlighten their minds and let them see.'*

- Confession: When you express your sorrow and seek repentance from God. *'God, forgive me; I am so sorry.'*

- Lamentation: Crying out to God in misery and brokenness. *'God, I am a miserable soul. I am no good. I don't know why You would love me. But Lord, I need You now!'*

- Adoration: Giving honor and praise to God. *'God, You are so wonderful, so grand, so powerful.'*

- Invocation: Summoning the presence of God in your life. *'God, be with me now and always.*

Obviously there is overlap between and among these various types of prayer. Again, this is not an exhaustive list, but only representative of the most common types of prayer.

True and False Prayer

Not all that you call prayer is true prayer. True prayer is a genuine impulse of God-consciousness, the knowledge that God is here with you now. Prayer is the mature request for moral growth and spiritual power, a wholehearted yearning to find God. But some of what you may call prayer is not prayer at all. False prayer may be a selfish request for unfair advantage over others.

False prayer might also be an angry cry for vengeance, your internal screech demanding that God punish someone to make things more equitable in your own eyes. God loves and cherishes all equally; to pray for unequal treatment for some over others would confound the purpose of prayer. True prayer seeks forgiveness, is based on God's wisdom, and enhances self-control.

Requests for curing your illness might be another category of unfair prayer. God's kingdom is not of this world, and to offer wealth, power, fame, or any other "human" desire of the body beyond your necessities is of no consequence to God. Such prayer is shortsighted, unilluminated, and wholly lacking in spiritual understanding.

Prayer is sometimes used as a substitute for action. Either through slothfulness, or some other means, you may avoid doing anything to help yourself or the situation—simply injecting prayer into the problem and thinking that your responsibility is fulfilled. This is not the prayer of hope of a God-connecting person of faith; rather it is an example of presumption, the compulsion of hope.

One of my favorite prayers is what I call the "Personality Prayer" because it addresses all six functions of a healthy personality:

God you are ...

the source of my belief...

the eyes with which I see...

the mind with which I think...

the heart in which I feel...

the will with which I choose...

and the strength in which I act.

Centering Prayer of Awareness

Words may be less important in prayer than you may think. God listens to the desires of your soul, what is in your heart, rather than the eloquent and melodious words you choose to use to express your heart's desires. In the ground-breaking book <u>Finding Grace at the Center</u> (Keating, Pennington & Clarke; St. Bede's Publications, Petersham, MA, 1978) Frs. Keating, Pennington, and Clarke offer a new and interesting type of prayer.

This new type of prayer is inspired by the 14th century book by an unknown English author, <u>The Cloud of Unknowing</u>. The prayer is one of contemplation, a prayer of quiet. The name given to this new prayer type is "centering prayer", named after the work of Thomas Merton. "In his writings he stressed that the simplest way to come into contact with the living God is to go to one's center and from there pass into God." (page 9).

In his book <u>Silence on Fire</u> (The Crossroad Publishing Co., New York, NY, 1991) William H. Shannon introduces a new type which is an extension of the centering prayer. Shannon describes "the prayer of awareness" as "...wordless prayer ... silence ...but a silence that is rich. It is the prayer of quiet rising out of solitude in which we seek to deepen our awareness of God's presence in our lives... in which we experience our total dependence on God and our <u>awareness</u> that we are in God. Wordless prayer is not an effort to `get anywhere', for we are already there in God's Presence."

God is everywhere, you cannot limit spirituality; every place is a sacred place. Regardless of where you may be, it is your place of holiness, your sacred ground. I have been in many, many hospital rooms and walked the halls of many nursing homes where I could feel the hallowedness of God present. Shannon says that *"our great spiritual need is to be in the presence of God.... and being alive to that fact."* (page 32). In order to be in God's presence, you need to become increasingly aware of the presence of God in everyone and everything. This is not a Pollyannaish way of living; on the contrary it is central to your faith that God is omnipresent. Your job is to seek God, to awaken to God, to be ever on the lookout for God at every stage and phase of your life.

In your time of illness you are called to accomplish so much:

1. Integrate the wisdom of your years, lest you fall into personal confusion and character fragmentation.

2. Let go of pretense and uncover the source of wonder and beauty, lest you slip into anger and irritability.

3. Take stock of all the gifts you have received and used in your life, or risk descent into dependency and despondency.

4. Discover the creative completion in your life, or else face helplessness and infantilization.

These tasks of your illness time become the sacred ground, the hallowed spaces of your existence. The prayer of awareness helps you to bring God into all this "life work" and generate a new vision of who and what you actually are, unencumbered by the busyness of the world. Your advancing spirituality is the theme which runs like a golden thread through all these developmental tasks of your illness time. It is this thread which not only holds you together as you move through illness, but it is also this thread which gives illness living its central purpose.

The Benefits of Prayer

The most basic prayer we can pray may be:

'Not my will, but Your Will be done.'

Prayer is a means whereby you can come closer and closer to aligning with God, of turning away from the distractions and distortions of the material world that pull, push, punish, and pander to you unceasingly. Without prayer, God is out of reach. It is only through prayer that you can come to more fully understand the nature of God's Will for you. Prayer is not a process for getting your own way; rather it is a process for taking God's way. Prayer is your connection with God, a process that allows you to better bear the fruits of the Spirit.

> *Prayer is not a process for getting your own way;*
> *rather it is a process for taking God's way.*

Prayer enriches your life by sustaining you now and all through your illness time of need. Prayer enlarges your capacity for loving and expands your insight, and your self-awareness; all of which attacks fear. Prayer augments your internal resources so you can ease your tension and remove conflict. Prayer equips you with confidence to follow the lead of the Spirit. It gives you courage to face the problems of life by renewing your mind. Prayer seeks new wisdom and energy, it gathers strength for you, and offers you better ways of adjusting to the problems of living. In short, prayer deepens your purpose in living. If there is one thing that you need desperately in your time of illness, it is purpose.

Prayer is not a luxury of your illness time, nor is it drudgery. Instead, prayer is an expanding personality requirement that never stops giving, and which fires your motivation so you can live your life to the fullest.

Some of the Personal Benefits of Prayer

Prayer offers you wealth untold! So much of what prayer offers you simply does not go recognized immediately, and perhaps you won't ever recognize its total value.

1. Gathering insight and wisdom: Prayer can offer you a positive introspective window into yourself. It can clarify your internal vision, offering not only the time to consider yourself, but also a new lens through which you can come to recognize your true self. In this way you also gain wisdom and new understandings about yourself.

2. Collecting energy for spiritual guidance: Prayer does seem to give more energy. Whether this new energy is actually translated into more "pep" during the day, or whether this energy simply comes from being more self-possessed.

3. Deepens purpose of living: Prayer helps you experience personal meaning in life. By keeping "in touch" with the Divine, you come to know more clearly the purpose of your life. You can be more confident that you are moving along the right path. Having a firm grip on your life purpose creates a wonderful gift: experiencing meaning in life.

4. Gain new and better ways of adjusting to meet problems of living: Prayer seems to stimulate the creative "juices" in your life. You may not become so rigid in your attitude and consequently stuck in your ways; prayer helps you become more malleable and flexible.

5. Enhanced insight into everything vital and real: Prayer helps you to recognize what is important and what is not. It helps you give proper priority to the various arenas of your life and hence find a most growthful and satisfying balance that otherwise wouldn't be there if prayer was not a vitalizing part of your life.

6. Relaxation of body and renewal of mind: During your illness time, you regularly need to "go to the well of refreshment." Prayer by its very nature removes you from the world, if only temporarily, and takes you to God where ultimate peace and the great calm of heaven can be found. You seek relaxation in so many places and people in this world, until you come to understand that true relaxation can only come from God.

7. Illumination for the soul: Prayer can beam the light of Christ onto your most noble parts. Prayer nourishes your soul and enables you to care for it with kindness and mercy. With prayer you can come to know your soul, the inner most part of you that bridges you to God. Without prayer, you flounder in a sea of darkness where you can lose your spiritual bearings and crash.

8. Courage to meet the problems of living: Living in this world is difficult. This is especially so when the illness process begins to attack you with its losses. You need courage to live and to grow; you need courage and fortitude to persevere in the face of uncertainty. You know that perfect love casts out fear, yet who among us has developed perfect love? You are therefore in fear to some degree most of the time. Courage comes from touching God regularly in prayer.

9. Self-understanding which attacks fear: Prayer gives you the pause required to come to a fuller understanding of who you really are. You cannot be true to yourself if you don't really know who you are. Prayer lets you look deeply into yourself

and come up with new facts about yourself that otherwise you might overlook.

10. <u>Relieve tension, remove conflict, and augment internal resources</u>: Prayer eases and soothes; it provides a spiritual comfort that is indescribable. In prayer you come to see your personal conflicts more clearly so you can take more appropriate and accurate action. Prayer helps you marshal your gifts of love which God has granted to each of us uniquely.

11. <u>Enlarge your capacity for living</u>: Prayer allows you to live with the magnitude of God and not become trapped in the confinements of this world. No matter where you may be, regardless of the prison that may confine you in worldly terms, you are always free when in prayer to soar into God's vast domain. This is not a freedom to simply escape the rigors of this world; rather, this is a freedom to transcend the trials and tribulations that the world places upon you.

12. <u>Strength to sustain you now and in your hour of need</u>: Prayer provides you with power, the power of God. It fortifies you with perseverance and steadfastness, power virtues that can convert you from spinelessness into having the true "spiritual grit" necessary to surmount whatever detour the world gives.

Spiritual Strengths Healing Prayers

The book <u>Prayers for Spiritual Strength...Physical Illnesses, Emotional Broken Places, and/or Spiritual Dis-eases</u> is the Spiritual Strengths Healing Plan series centerpiece book on prayer. It contains 90 formal prayers all together—one prayer for each of the 30 spiritual strengths as well as one for each of the accompanying 30 shadows and 30 compulsions. These prayers are part of a 7-Week Healing Immersion Program patients receive during the Spiritual Strengths Healing Retreat.

During the 7-Week Immersion Program, you're instructed to focus on the prayers for your six premier spiritual strengths as well as their accompanying shadows and compulsions. Many Spiritual Strengths participants find a new healing horizon when they devote 30 days (basically one month) to the task. They not only recite the morning, afternoon, and evening prayers for each strength on a daily basis but they also embroider this with enhancements to broaden and deepen their prayer experience.

First, they let the words of the prayer trickle over them slowly as though they were standing under a soothing warm shower. They imagine the streams of the shower as rivulets of healing grace—power that invigorates and strengthens all the healing mechanisms, known and unknown, within them. They might stay with this prayerful poise for 10-15 minutes breathing for relaxation and repeating a word or phrase in the prayer that they find particularly appealing.

This method of praying is structured but doesn't stricture you into a repetitive rut; it lets you take the lead; it gives you the tools to find a new internal balance and a much deepened appreciation of how effective prayer can be. The recitation of an appealing work or phrase that you have selected from the prayer gives you a new invigoration of choice that settles your soul with a revived sense of potency.

Self-Care Technique Four

Imagination and Guided Imagery

<u>Imagination</u> brings figures, circumstances, events, and relationships into sharp focus. Imagination generally involves projecting into the future to "see" how you would like some future event to take place.

<u>Guided imagery</u> refers to placing yourself in another dimension and seeing yourself in a situation that is far removed from your normal lifestyle.

There is great overlap between imagination and guided imagery. However, imagination deals with the realm of the possible, or at least probable, while fantasy deals with the impossible.

The modern use of therapeutic imagery usually entails a 20 - 25 minute session beginning with a relaxation exercise to help focus your attention and to find your spiritual center. During a typical session of imagery, you focus on a predetermined image designed to help you control a particular symptom or you allow your mind to conjure up images that give you insight into a particular problem. Depending on your needs, imagery can be explored on your own, or with the help of recordings. It's helpful to use as many senses as possible during a guided imagery session.

Visualization

Move yourself to a comfortable and quiet place. In your mind's eye visualize your brokenness (where you need healing),

45

whatever it may be: physical, emotional, relational, psychological, or spiritual.

Once you have a good mental picture of your brokenness, try to dip into what the brokenness feels like. It's not necessary to use words to describe the feeling, just try to experience the sensation of the feeling. Usually some form of pain accompanies brokenness. On the material level, pain is physical; on other levels, the pain is generally psychic or spiritual. Try to "get in touch" with this pain whatever form it may take.

There are four major characteristics of imagery that make it particularly valuable in healing. Imagery can—

- Produce physical changes.

- Provide psychological insight.

- Enhance emotional awareness.

- Induce spiritual clarity.

These four characteristics are described in more depth below:

1. Physical change. Imagery can affect the body directly. If you try to salivate by simply telling yourself to do so, you'll probably fail. But if you imagine you are eating a lemon, you'll probably succeed.

2. Psychological insight. Pain can be successfully addressed with imagery by connecting the pain with some mental image that may represent some confusion or conflict you're experiencing. The pain of anxiety or minor depression may be connected with stress from work, distress of sickness, or the pain of loss, for example. Try to describe your pain with the most descriptive words you can find. Now close your eyes, move from relaxation to focusing on those words and be patient as an image emerges in your mind's eye. This image is your healing image.

46

3. Emotional Awareness. Imagery is one of the quickest and most direct ways to become aware of your emotional state and its potential for healing. Let yourself relax. Imagine what your illness looks like. Come up with a specific image that may capture the shadows or compulsion that may be in some ways blocking your healing.

4. Spiritual Clarity. Follow the instructions below to realize how imagery can induce spiritual clarity.

Spiritual Strengths Points of Light

Visualize each of your six strengths as points of healing light. Each of these points of light is luminous, shining from the inside out. Each point represents the power of one of your spiritual strengths, one of your six premier virtues that flows as grace directly and only from God. Each point of light is the manifest presence of grace.

Believing

Your believing spiritual strength (God-Reliance, Humility, Acceptance, Mercy, or Hope) point of light is normally found in your belief core. In bodily terms your belief core can be seen as the **crown at the very top of your head**. This spot has been associated with the entry point of grace, God's healing power. Saints are depicted with halos seemingly floating above their heads as a sign of their very well developed faith; halos can also be seen as a reflection of a super-illuminated belief core. Another indication of an illuminated, grace animated belief core is the tongues of fire above the Apostles' heads at Pentecost.

Perceiving

Your perceiving strength (Vision, Humor, Peace, Adaptability, or Simplicity) point of light can normally be seen as residing in **your eyes**, a single point in the middle of each eyeball. These points of light allow you to see yourself (insight) and the world (outlook) through the eyes of Christ.

Thinking

Your thinking strength (Faith, Wisdom, Steadfastness, Wholeness, or Charity) point of light resides in the **center of your brain**, the seat of thinking. This light illuminates your thoughts so that you think with the mind of Christ.

Feeling

Your feeling strength (Joy, Trust, Love-Finder, Empathy, and Gratitude) point of light resides in **your heart** and roams freely through your cardio-vascular system. This point of light cleanses you from feelings that can disturb your peace of heart and mind.

Deciding

Your deciding strength (Harmony, Patience, Strength, Transcendence, or Self-Discipline) point of light resides in **your gut, right** behind your belly button. Gut reactions are quick decisions. This deciding point of light (grace) roams your GI tract from top to bottom seeking choices that are not of God.

Acting

Your acting strength (Truth, Inspiration, Kindness, Courage, or Perseverance) point of light resides in five places: **your palms, your feet, and your tongue**. You perform actions with your hands, you move yourself with your feet, and you speak with your tongue. Your acting point of light helps you do what Jesus would do, go where he would go, say what he would say.

You can visualize each of these six points of light roaming around the various sites in your body—searching for beliefs, perceptions, thoughts, feelings, choices, and actions that are not reflective of your strengths and illuminating them with sufficient light from God (grace) to eradicate them, leaving you cleansed and healed of these invading and illness-producing invaders, known as **shadows and compulsions**.

How to Practice

In your mind's eye, position one (or more) of your spiritual strengths points of light at the site of your pain or other brokenness. If your pain or other point of healing is physical, then place the point of light at the center of that pain. If the pain is emotional or relational, then place one of your points of light at the center of your heart. If the pain is spiritual, place one of your points of light at the center of your inner altar, or your soul (you'll have to imagine these as well).

Here are some examples ...

Physical Pain of Illness

Mentally place one of your points of light right in the center of the pained area and imagine that the spiritual strength point of light glows brightly there and gradually overtakes the dark pain with its brightness. This may take 10-20 minutes, although with practice it will not take that long, naturally depending on the severity of the pain.

Physical Brokenness

Again mentally place one of your points of light at the center of the illness site. Imagine the point of light glowing brightly and sending out rays from itself that find, envelop and heal the site. Then imagine that the spiritual strength point of light draws the brokenness into itself and ingests it—converting the brokenness into new healthy tissue that it now replaces in the surrounding tissue. If you have illness in multiple sites in your body, then you can use more than one virtue point of light at a time. You can even station the points of light at these sites all day long to increase the benefit of the healing process.

Emotional Brokenness

Anger caused by Illness

Quiet your mind and heart...breathe deeply...breathe in the power of God (spiritual strengths) and exhale any toxins coming from your anger. Settle yourself. Imagine one of your points of light settling in the center of your forehead. Imagine it radiating out healing rays that travel through space directly to the forehead of the person (you might be angry at a situation, thing, circumstance, relationship, etc., but try to identify a single person with whom your anger is most associated) with whom you are experiencing anger. Imagine those healing rays penetrating into the mind and heart of that one person. As you are "seeing" this happen, say to yourself: *'May you be happy. May you be well. May you be filled with love.'* Repeat this over and over for some time all the while maintaining the image of the healing rays emanating from the virtue point of light in the center of your forehead and traveling to the center of the forehead of the person with whom you are experiencing anger.

Fear Caused by Illness

Humankind knows how to fear; it seems we are never far from fear. We spend enormous amounts of our energy, both physical and psychic, trying to keep fear at bay (think government, insurance companies, banks, armies, the justice system, prisons, preventive medicine, rules, laws, anti-aging crème, etc., etc.). Fear seems a permanent part of the interior human landscape. Yet fear can at times become so, well...fearsome, that it threatens to overtake you in waves of anxiety, and even panic.

Imagine positioning one of your spiritual strengths points of light at your fear center. Some people think of the mind (brain) as their fear center, others think of the heart. I guess it's possible to think of any part of the body as your fear center. Wherever you "see" your center of fear, place one of your points of light there. Imagine that God's infinite power flows through this point of light. See your fear as darkness, and the point of light as God's eternal healing grace. No light is brighter than God; this light overcomes the darkness of your fear. As the light gradually becomes brighter and brighter your fear is gradually erased, overcome by the wondrous glow from God through your virtue point of light. When the light comes it drives out the darkness, and this is exactly what's happening in you; God's sacred illumination overcomes all your darkness.

Psychological Brokenness

Depression Caused by Illness

Depression and sickness are unfortunately very commonly found together. Depression can envelop you in a cocoon of egocentric darkness. Your thoughts are all centered on your illness, which are generally all depressing. Nothing seems good, or fair, or peaceful, or loving...everything seems exactly the opposite of these. God seems distant. You are tempted to listen only to your shadows and compulsions and ignore your strengths. Depression is the flipside of your true self, the antithesis of who you truly are. Depression robs you of healing (see Healing and Depression, one of the books in the Spiritual Strengths Healing Plan series).

Where in your body do you most feel your depression? Is it in your brain, your forehead, your achy muscles, your gut, or your heart? Perhaps you feel your depression in all these places at various times or at the same time? Wherever you most feel your depression, "place" one of your points of light right there. Imagine the luminous point of light sending out its healing rays filling the darkness of depression with celestial illumination. If you feel your depression in more than one place, then go ahead and place another point of light at this site. You can place all six of your points of light in various places in your body if you choose.

Anxiety

Anxiety is the accumulation of layers of emotional insecurity that becomes so distressing that it crosses the line from an emotional discomfort to a psychological disorder. At the base of anxiety, in whatever variety it manifests in you, is fear. To "treat" your anxiety you can follow the directions above regarding fear; the same principles apply.

Relationship Brokenness

Unfortunately the ravages of illness can even negatively affect relationships, even your marriage. The stress and distress of illness can put relationships at risk by having partners carry heavy, and sometimes contradictory emotional burdens including: fear, anxiety, disengagement, resentment, criticism, remorse, defensiveness, doubt, indifference, lack of forgiveness, and many more.

Such feelings are more common than not in relationships dealing with illness. They can cause chronic, pervasive, and debilitating pain that is not only damaging to the relationship but also to the individual partners, as well as children, friends, extended family, and really anyone who touches the relationship. (NOTE: See my book Loving for a Lifetime, for a thorough description of how to use the Spiritual Strengths Method to bring healing to troubled marriages.)

Each of the partners in the marriage relationship possesses six premier spiritual strengths. Regardless of how underdeveloped the spiritual strengths may be, they are still present in some form. The goal of the marriage, and indeed its sublime richness, is that partners are called to offer their own spiritual strengths to and for their partner. Ideally and over time, marriage partners embed their own spiritual strengths into each other.

When this embedding process happens it creates a new unit consisting of 12 strengths (six from each partner) equally resident in each partner—becoming one in spirit. Each partner is supposed to do all he/she can to foster the growth of their partner's strengths. But the stresses and pressures of illness can contort many marriages to such a degree that this level of sharing and support is invaded. Pain grows in the empty spaces created when their partner's gift are not sufficiently offered and received by the other, when a necessary level of sharing (intimacy) is not practiced. What to do?

It would be best to practice this exercise together with your partner. But when this is impossible for whatever reason, then it can be practiced alone with good result. Sit quietly; take several (or more) deep breaths bringing you to a centered condition. Imagine your six Spiritual Strengths healing points of light, representing your six spiritual strengths, growing stronger with each calming breath you take.

When you're ready, imagine your healing points of light, one by one, dividing into two points of light as by some mystical organic division process. Imagine one of the pair of each of your six points of light releasing from your body and flying over to your partner's body, and there taking up residence in bright illumination. Now imagine that your partner's six healing points of light are likewise dividing and flying over to your body taking up residence with you.

Now each partner has 12, not just six, healing points of light. The best and strongest healing points of light of each partner now reside in each other and stand ready to bring new animation and energy to the relationship. Imagine the points of light swirling and penetrating to every corner, fold, and crevice of your body.

Imagine the points of light from your partner bringing new light and increased energy to you in ways you never imagined before. Stay with this advancing image for some time, perhaps 10 to 20 minutes.

Spiritual Brokenness

We live holistically, as a marvelous and God-designed integration of body, and mind, and spirit. To some degree each one of these three affects the other two, i.e., a) body affects mind and spirit; b) mind affects body and spirit; and c) spirit affects body and mind. When the physical body is invaded by sickness, then the mind and the spirit are likewise attacked. Illness then often causes us to suffer from a spiritual dis-ease in a like manner that it can cause emotional, psychological, and/or relational disease.

Spiritual brokenness emerges in us when we don't devote sufficient energy to fully accomplish the spiritual "work" of our illness journey. Our spiritual work is generally coming to spiritual grips with the illness, by exercising virtue, by practicing the ministry of presence, by coming to terms with the stark reality of the world, and by seeking new ways to learn how to love better than before our illness. This of course is no small order! When we address these spiritual developmental tasks and are relatively successful in accomplishing them, we can enter into a new stage of spiritual growth. However, when we are not successful, for whatever reasons, we suffer consequences that are far greater than simply missing out on the spiritual growth; we instead fall into a spiritual pain, or what I call *spiritual diseases of the soul*. Here are very short descriptions:

Spiritual Lifelessness

When we become fixated, we become vulnerable to spiritual lifelessness. This is not the lifelessness of self-surrender, or the self-abandonment of a spiritual mystic; no, this is the lifelessness of self-nihilism and existential barrenness, a spiritual nothingness well beyond the aridity of the "dark night of the soul." This is a lifelessness characterized by "being stuck in fear," a state where we can no longer taste the sweet "newness" of Jesus. We lose our inner potency and adopt the role of illness victim.

Disconnected Arrogance

Disconnected arrogance is a spiritual disease driven by a disregard for the intangibles of life. Those who suffer with this disease place themselves as the final authority of life and living. They see no need to consult others, discuss, or interact with an openness of mind and heart; they become fatalistic. For them, all things are already decided by their illness. Consequently they cannot enter into the mystery of life, the Pascal mystery of death and rebirth, or the numinous (soul) aspects of living. Underneath this bravado, however, may lurk a basic insecurity that motivates the sufferer toward aggressiveness as a means of "conquering" innate doubts, questions, and conflicts.

Consummate Fault Finding

Consummate fault finding is a form of spiritual distress that occurs when people are unable to find sources of meaning, hope, love, peace, comfort, strength, and/or connection in life, or when they are unsuccessful in reconciling their basic beliefs about God with the illness in their life. The distress can have detrimental effects on physical and mental health.

Some symptoms of consummate fault finding are anger that's hidden in a form of righteous indignation; rudeness in the sense of a flagrant disregard for other people's rights, and especially their feelings; cynicism, seeing little hope for the human condition in general and a tacit rejection of attempts by others to make things better; being sharply unpleasant and disagreeable, focusing only on what's wrong...to name but a few.

Whatever the spiritual disease or brokenness, the Spiritual Strengths Healing Plan is somewhat the same. Again, first you learn to move to a centered, calm, relaxed, and relatively stress-free condition. Once you achieve this, then you imagine your six Spiritual Strengths points of light rotating around each other forming something of a luminous circular disk; some people even see this as an illuminated circular saw blade. Imagine this disk slowly moving around your body breaking up long solidified, even calcified nodules of hurt that have collected in every fold and crevice of the body, mind, and spirit. Imagine that as these nodules of hurt are dislodged, you gradually (and this may require a series of sessions) relax from the inside out and eventually lose your need to demonstrate the compensatory symptoms of the spiritual brokenness.

It's important while envisioning the luminous blade slowly making its round through the body, to say a short prayer repetitively. One suggestion is to take the italicized sentences at the beginning of the prayers you find in Prayers for Spiritual Strength, and repeat these over and over as you visualize the movement of the luminous disk.

Self-Care Technique Five

The Healing Value of Smiling

NOTE: The following is excerpted from: <u>The Power of Smiling: Using Positive Psychology for Optimal Health & Healing</u>, one of the books in the Spiritual Strengths Healing Plan series.

The Positive Effects of a Simple Smile

Can smiling affect your mood...your health...your soul? Psychological research that looks at the effects of smiling seems to arrive at a universal conclusion: smiling is the key to a positive outlook on life.   The positive effects of smiling are legion: improved immune function, increased tolerance for pain and frustration, lowered stress and blood pressure, and even higher levels of creativity.

The Basic Tenets of Positive Psychology Correlated with Smiling

Positive psychologists have discovered smiling is a powerful tool that can—

- Shift our basic beliefs from ones of scarcity to ones of abundance. A smile can move us away from deficits in ourselves and toward a search for our strengths. Smiling can shift our vision so that instead of seeing potential obstacles, we now see challenges that are intrinsically motivating.

- Help re-draw a new picture of living that galvanizes our attention and vitalizes our unique resources.

- Develop a "strengths vision" so we can see what is creative, what is resourceful, and what is integrated in us. Smiling lets us see a more global picture, and accents the positive traits and creative qualities in our personality.

- Focus our mind's eye to see what's "worked" for us in the past and shape our efforts around these motivated abilities.

- Help us speak from our "strengths voice" and speak to our own internal "strengths receptors."

- Allow us to appreciate what thrills us; a smile offers us a sense of awe, wonder, and delight. A smile activates us to use our own emotional intelligence so we can engage in a search for those emotions that energize and animate us, rather than focusing on those emotions that paralyze us.

- Let us generate "action options" that "move and stir" our core desires and develop goals that create challenge, objectives that serve the goals, and strategies for achieving all this.

- Promote personal engagement. Smiling helps us animate our desires into action; a smile allows us to always be "working on" improving ourselves.

The Power of Smiling

Dr. Mark Stibich, Ph.D. offers us ten general ways that smiling affects us positively: relationally, emotionally, behaviorally, and psychologically. (For more information, go to http://longevity.about.com/od/lifelongbeauty/tp/smiling.htm.)

Smiling—

- Makes us more attractive. We are drawn to people who smile. Frowns, scowls, and grimaces all push people away, but a smile draws them in.

- Changes our mood. It's hard to be "moody" when we're wearing a smile. A smile can "trick" our bodies into shifting our mood in a positive direction.

- Is contagious. A smile brightens up all those around us; it makes our lives happier.

- Relieves stress. Smiling saves us from appearing tired, worn down, and overwhelmed—all of which increase our internal stress levels.

- Boosts our immune system. Our immune system is hyper-sensitive to our mood; when we smile, we boost our mood which also strengthens our immune system making us less vulnerable to everything from colds and flu to infections of all types—even illness.

- Lowers our blood pressure. When we reduce our stress, we experience a corresponding decrease in hypertension (high blood pressure).

- Releases endorphins, natural painkillers, and serotonin. All of these are chemicals that our bodies naturally produce. Endorphins increase our overall sense of well-being. Natural painkillers fight pain of all types, and serotonin regulates our mood.

- Injects more tone, freshness, and vibrancy into our appearance. Smiling shapes our faces in such a way that we look younger. Smiling works like a natural face lift. Smiling is an anti-gravity "miracle drug" that re-sculpts our facial muscles and gives us a new vitality.

- Makes us seem successful. Smiling raises our confidence level, gives us enhanced self-esteem, and improves our overall poise; all these give us an air of success.

- Helps us stay positive. Smiling is our best "attitude adjustment." It's hard to think of something negative when we're smiling.

Smiling and Your Spiritual Life

While all of the benefits of smiling are rather dramatic and certainly give you powerful reasons for remembering to smile, the central question is: Can smiling affect you at the deeper levels of your life, even at your spiritual level? Both my professional and personal experience tells me that smiling can stimulate a more profound updraft on your spiritual life than it does even on your physical, social, or psychological life arenas.

Your smile literally moves you...a smile touches your heart and shifts your personality. But most curiously, even a tiny smile is not insignificant on a spiritual level either. This most simple human action, the common, everyday action of a smile, generates the most immense effects. It opens up the portals of your real self, the sacred doorways of God's power and might through which flow the celestial grace-power that is ever available to you, but which so many times you are indifferently or inadvertently unaware of. Even the most diminutive and common smile touches the innermost and tender parts of your inner core; it transforms you with the energy of heaven, that intangible place called your soul.

Smiling inspires your personality and transforms your life.

While all 35 "smile-wisdoms" in the book <u>The Power of Smiling</u> can relate, directly or not, to your illness journey, I've selected the ones here that are most directly relatable to your walk with illness.

When I smile, I remember my spiritual strengths.

God has invested "power and might" in me uniquely.

My job is to come to a clearer understanding of these most purposeful strengths and to do my very best to express them out to the world.

Smiling gives me pause to remember that indeed I have been endowed by God; I have been given God's "power and might" right here right now.

Smiling serves as my behavioral cue that I am continuously called to "be" in my spiritual strengths—to immerse myself in them and to saturate my personality with them.

When I smile, I can make better choices.

Choices are everywhere in my world — developing strategies, selecting goals and objectives, uncovering options, and constructing plans are all part of the personality function of making decisions.

Smiling gives me a quiet internal realization that the common everyday choices I make actually determine the kind of world I live in.

Smiling alerts me that I need never give away my free will choice to persons or forces that inhibit my forward spiritual growth.

Smiling gently nudges me toward aligning my will with God's will, and therein finding the healthiest and the most abundant way of living.

I am best when I choose God's way, God's relationship, and God's values as my guiding principles for living fully...smiling helps me in that quest.

When I smile, I activate my internal healing system.

I know that the most powerful healing generator in all the cosmos is right within me.

Medications, surgery, exercise, stress reduction, healthy relationships, etc., are all factors in the equation for healing, but the glue that holds it all together is faith, and my smile confirms my bedrock faith.

Jesus always told the people whom he healed that it was their faith that healed them. I believe that Jesus smiled when he said those words.

Carrying a smile with me on my journey stimulates all the mechanisms for healing in me: my immune system, indeed all the systems of my body, my centered personality, my beliefs, attitudes and values, and much more.

In short, my smile pulls me toward that most valued gift from God...the gift of faith, the ultimate healing power there is.

When I smile, I immediately feel better.

Like you, I always seek to feel good. I want to feel "up" and energetic, sharp and "with it," and positive and useful.

Smiling seems to put a shine on my day, a hop in my step, and an inspiration in my heart.

Feelings are the emotional "facts" of the moment, and a smile focuses on the most vitalizing emotional facts that are present in any situation if you look hard enough.

Smiling doesn't mean that I'm a fraud, that I'm a Pollyanna—always needing to see only the good things and only allowing positive feelings in.

Smiling energizes me so that I don't overlook those fantastic flashes of true reality, those intangible facets of the Presence that elevate me and bring me home. A smile helps me begin to understand the magnificence of wholeness in reality, and wholeness feels good!

When I smile, irritation and frustration begins to drain away.

I feel irritated and frustrated because I give myself thoughts that are not totally whole.

I get a distorted picture of reality because I can only see through the glass darkly.

Consequently I can form distorted thoughts from this distorted reality, which in turn generates irritation and frustration (and so many other paralyzing emotions).

When I put on a smile, I break this morbid cycle.

My smile soothes me; it calms my ragged emotions and lets me see through the glass clearly.

Smiling releases me from noxious emotions that contort my life.

Smiling gives me the freedom to be more than I thought I was.

Smiling lifts me up above the distractions of the world to a new emotional space of peace and calm.

When I smile, my pain and brokenness is easier to bear.

I am broken in ways both known and unknown to me.

Brokenness causes me pain on many levels: physical, emotional, familial, psychological, and/or spiritual.

Sometimes this brokenness threatens to overpower me, to take control of me.

Smiling lets me reclaim myself, lets me exert power over the pain and brokenness.

Smiling allows me to turn the tables as it were on the pain and brokenness, and once again take the reins of my life back, as opposed to letting pain control my life.

Smiling is the therapeutic antidote of choice for any and all of my pain and brokenness.

Naturally I want to consult with and use the tools of the medical community, yet if I do this with a frown rather than a smile, I undermine its potential benefit for me.

When I smile, I feel energized.

My smile activates a jolt of joy that pulsates through my body, mind, and soul like an uplifting impulse of energy.

My smile reminds me that I am part of the greatness of creation, and that all I encounter today is as well.

My smile-induced joy allows me to see beyond what formerly snagged my mind and heart and brought me "down."

My smile lets me see the beauty that's right in front of me ...beauty that I may have otherwise overlooked.

My smile ignites an updraft of inspiration and a free-spirited lightness in me that propels me forward with a renewed determination and a refortified confidence.

Joy elevates my heart; it gives me a positive attitude and an inner balance knowing that God's grace sustains me always.

Self-Care Technique Six

Healing with Art and Crafts

Arts & crafts therapy is a way of expressing specific emotional or physical issues through art...it is not about creating a fantastic piece of art; indeed you need no artistic talent at all. Art therapy aims to help you express yourself in a safe environment, using art materials in a way that have a positive effect on your personal growth in addition to a therapeutic effect on your illness.

Art therapists believe that being creative helps you heal. They believe that arts & crafts can tap into emotions and abilities beyond your everyday awareness. They say you can access these through different forms of art & crafts therapy.

Art & crafts therapy can help you heal in many ways—

1. Encouraging expression of emotions, which can improve your relationship with others.

2. Encouraging creativity and self-confidence.

3. Helping control anxiety, depression, and low self-esteem.

4. Helping distract your mind from pain or discomfort.

Arts & crafts therapy is used to help people in many areas of their lives including:

1. Chronic or life limiting illnesses.

2. Mental health problems, including depression and addiction.

3. Relationship problems.

Art & Crafts Therapy and Illness

The most prominent reason that art therapy is used with chronically ill patients is to help them feel better and more positive: to help express emotions; cope with grief, fear, depression and anxiety; achieve a sense of creative freedom and gain self-confidence. Some people find it easier to access deeper emotions simply by talking things over.

Dr. Bernie Siegel, who uses this technique extensively in his "exceptional patient" workshops, says in his book <u>Love, Medicine and Miracles</u>, *"The drawings are a wonderful way to get people to open up and talk about things they would otherwise conceal."* Dr. Siegel asks patients to draw any scenes from their life that they like, but he especially asks patients to draw themselves, their treatment, their disease, and their own body's way of eliminating their disease.

As a complementary therapy to medical treatment, art therapy has shown to reduce negative effects of illness diagnosis and treatment. According to the American Illness Society, art therapy enables a patient to relieve fear, anger, stress, and anxiety through expressing emotions. Art therapists believe the therapy chemically affects the brain as well, releasing feel-good chemicals in the brain and altering brain waves affecting emotions.

Arts & Crafts Therapy Research and Illness

In a study published in the Oncology Nursing Forum that looked at how breast illness patients express feelings about their illness, researchers found that art can capture the most intimate and personal aspects of the illness experience. Most studies centered on the value of arts & crafts to help patients deal with the pain and emotional trauma associated with sickness.

In her book <u>Art Therapy Sourcebook</u>, Cathy A. Malchiodi writes about an ovarian cancer patient who used ink drawing to create an abstract image entitled *Woman Caught in a Spiral, Spinning Round and Round*. This image was based on the turbans that the patient wore due to chemotherapy hair loss. Malchiodi states that "while the drawing did not magically cure the depression about her cancer and the effects of powerful medical interventions, it allowed her a way to express feelings that were hard to convey to her family and friends and made it possible for us to talk about how she might be able to make changes in her life, given the impact of the illness recurrence." (eHow.com/about_5454528_illness-patients-art-drawing-therapy.html#1kbDZEs3B)

Many thanks to Brenda Lilliston, a very talented and dedicated Spiritual Strengths Healing Coach who created and offered the following on "Wisdom cards" to a group of persons who were already well aware of their unique spiritual strengths. I think this is brilliant.

Visual Art Exploration: Wisdom Cards

Materials needed: three medium-sized rectangle-shaped pieces of watercolor paper (about 5' x 7") watercolors, brush, jar of water, collage images, glue stick, pen, scissors and roll of drafting tape or masking tape.

Begin with some meditation.

In Letters to a Young Poet, Rainer Maria Rilke writes, "Have patience with everything unresolved in your heart and try to love the questions themselves…Live the questions now." ….The arts help us to dwell in that space of the question by allowing us to honor the images and feelings without having to move to linear and logical thinking, the thinking that wants to find answers.

Soul questions are those that speak to the deepest desires of our heart. They ask in different ways, "How am I seeking to create a meaningful life?" Phil Cousineau writes in The Art of Pilgrimage that the purpose behind questions is to initiate the quest."

Take some time in silence to reflect on what soul questions you want to ask of yourself, (your spiritual strengths/ compulsions/shadows) and/or inner artist.

These questions will initiate your inner quest through art. Write down one of each of these soul questions on the back of each piece of paper. (You should have three different questions and three pieces of paper.) Then shuffle the papers so you don't know which paper holds which question on the reverse. As you move into the visual-expression experience, let the questions go for the time being.

Take a roll of tape. With the tape, create a frame around the edges of each piece of paper to hold them down to the board.

Begin by taking some watercolors, brush, and small container of water and dip your brush in the water first, then the watercolors. Explore the colors you feel drawn to and cover the background surface. Try to release your analytical mind and return to your breath as an anchor in the present moment.

After a time of painting, shift your attention to cutting out collage images or words. As you sort through images, notice especially the ones that have resonance—a strong positive energetic draw—and the ones that have dissonance—a strong negative energetic resistance.

Select the images that stir this inner movement, without making judgments about whether they are the "right" ones. Gather images through which you experience resonance or dissonance, and create collages for each of the three cards, leaving as much of the painted background exposed as you would like.

Keep returning to your breath as a way to stay grounded in the present moment, allowing your intuition to guide the process of placing the images in relationship to one another. Notice what happens internally during the process.

When the three pieces are done, do not turn them over just yet. Take some time to reflect on the process of creating each card. What did you notice in yourself? What were the voices and judgments that arose?

Which of the collages felt the most freeing to create? Which one felt the most challenging?

After exploring the process for a time, take each image and turn it over to see which questions corresponds with which card. Notice your internal response as you discover what the synchronicity of images reveals about your question. Synchronicity sparks connections where we might not otherwise have seen them. See what wisdom in the images have to offer to you. Take some time to journal about your discoveries.

From The Artist's Rule: Nurturing Your Creative Soul with Monastic Wisdom by Christine Valters Paintner

Self-Care Technique Seven

Life Review and Spiritual Autobiography

Your personal life story is an adventure that needs to be lifted up as a unique rendition of how God's love "works" in the world. Your story has all the components of a spiritual bestseller: brokenness, redemption, forgiveness, transformation, enlightenment, more brokenness, tragedy, confusion, more forgiveness, and on and on the saga unveils the redemptive work of God. It's a love story of grand proportion. It's not until your illness time when you can capture these wondrous memories and quilt them into a masterful tapestry, although it may be something you couldn't have begun to create in earlier phases of your life. Here is the "stuff" of your life, the raw material that can be woven into the most beautiful garment you can "wear" as your own. In a sense this creation becomes your wisdom apparel, your own shawl of life which proudly proclaims how God's finger has been on you, guiding your life all along. (From the Introduction, All My Days, R. P. Johnson, Liguori Pub.)

The mental health community once viewed reminiscing as the idle wandering of a diminished, or at least diminishing, mind. Today we recognize fully that looking back and remembering past events in our lives is not only healthy but fun as well. The positive aspects of reminiscing have been incorporated into a concept known as *life review*. Life review is a quite normal behavior for which all of us can contribute. Life review, looking back on our lives, enables us to see life patterns and to develop life understandings that may otherwise go unnoticed.

Finding Personal Wisdom on Your Healing Journey

Sickness, Illness, and any unwanted transition are times when you seek your deeper self. You yearn for clearer perspectives, keener insight, and cleaner values. At such times you require a sharper image of yourself and of what is important to you. You may wonder, as you move through your illness time, what you really have learned in your life journey thus far; you may desire a more coordinated view of life, one that reflects the experience you've gathered so far. You seek ways of converting this experience into something more organized, coordinated, and orderly than its current disheveled state.

The time of illness has been called "the wisdom-making time." In between the pangs of illness, and perhaps because of them, you can unearth treasures heretofore unnoticed, gems of heart and mind, spirit and soul formerly buried that, now rest peacefully in your belief core while awaiting discovery.

Your personal life history is the repository of these riches. Such wealth, when deeply understood and seen through the eyes of faith, provides your underlying life script. Wisdom-making requires that you flesh-out and color this underlying script. As you do, you give your life meaning far beyond what you could have otherwise deciphered: you find wisdom!

Yet through what secret alchemy can you convert your desires for the sweetness of deeper understanding into actual, practical, and reliable life principles of wisdom that have the power to transform your life from day-to-day survival into an adventure of magnificent proportion? By what process can you discover the integrating factors that have given your life wholeness and completeness that you may not have realized was there?

Years ago during my college years, a friend of mine performed a rather unusual perceptual trick with himself. He imagined his life as a movie; naturally he played the star, the main character. He claimed that he could actually imagine the cameras rolling as he went about his life. Each day was a new episode in this ongoing serial; each life occurrence became a new scene in his personal movie. He liked reminding himself, as well as his friends, that he wasn't simply living a life; he was creating a cinematic masterpiece. To the rest of us, his life appeared quite normal; yet to him, his life was bursting with interest, intrigue, and imagination. In his eyes, there was nothing "normal" or "average" about his life whatsoever; in his eyes, he was truly living an adventure.

It strikes me now that my friend's notion, which seemed rather silly at the time, may actually have some application, however indirect, to your attempts at living a full life of faith during and after your illness time. Just as my friend was creating a "masterpiece" with his life, in his case a movie, are you not similarly called to create a masterpiece out of your life as well? Are you not living an adventure in faith during this time of illness?

What determines whether you see your life experiences merely as day-to-day occurrences of little consequence and significance, or whether you can see your life as bursting with interest, intrigue, and imagination on a faith level? In a sense, you too are involved in a saga, just like my college friend. You are creating a story of faith, a story that is certainly of movie script quality. If you learn to perceive your life in its full measure of spiritual drama, you too can create a masterpiece!

To develop this perspective, you must first teach yourself to view the events of your life as individual steps on your "staircase of faith." Your mental files contain all the information of your life. Every event, every relationship, every success, failure, thought, feeling, etc. is filed as memories in your huge personal data bank. Each of these events, etc. has served in some way, some much stronger than others, to shape and define you into who you are today.

The problem is that it's hard to gain such perspective; many of us live our lives only for today—using up most of our energy simply reacting to today's issues and everyday demands. When you continue to live like this, you lose the perspective on your life necessary for you to really see that you are indeed living a masterpiece of your own making.

No other person, no other force, no other anything can derail your ongoing creative powers; only you can forfeit them, if you so choose! In your younger years you were ill equipped and had little time to tease out whatever meaning there may have been for you in your daily routine. Yet, as you moved farther along in your lifespan, you gained much personal history (and hopefully some wisdom) as well as more time—necessary ingredients for a fuller discernment of the meaning of your life.

Spiritual Autobiography

Cultural ideas about sickness tend to be very regressive. They may lead you to believe that your life as a person with sickness is all about protecting your body, and being concerned with the physical form of your life alone; what you can see, taste, hear, touch, and smell. As a person of faith you know that your life is so much more than this. When you add your spirituality to life review you come up with a completely new concept: a spiritual autobiography. Here is a way you can touch your own inner life tenderly; here is the road to soul discovery.

Such "soul work" is essential for patients and chronic-sickness survivors of faith because it accomplishes all that a life review does plus so much more. It nourishes your inner being, it feeds your soul, and renews your spirit; it enhances your ability to perceive beyond the structure of lives, and enriches your relationship with others, with yourself, and with God.

Francis Dorff has written a sensitive book called <u>Simply Soul-Stirring</u> about how to write a spiritual autobiography (<u>Simply Soul-Stirring, Writing as a Meditative Practice</u>, New York, Paulist Press). This small book (only 84 pages) gives both the rationale for and tips on penning a spiritual autobiography. Dorff artfully and empathetically convinces us that writing is good for the soul. He maintains that our culture is toxic to our soul development; we must buttress ourselves with meditative practices that can spiritually "ground" us; and meditative writing is one of these practices. He encourages us to write daily.

This spiritual discipline can reward you with becoming ever more awake to the hand of God in every moment of your life. It can strengthen your mood, heighten your cheerfulness, and break through "hang-ups" that may have previously blocked you from seeing the richness and meaning in your daily life. He says that ... *"It [the book] is meant only as a simple primer to tempt and encourage you to see if the simple act of writing can stir your soul and help you live more soulfully."* (page 3). Dorff tells us that this kind of meditative life review writing comes from the inside, the inner places of your soul; he says writing this way is "simply soul stirring."

When you write like this, you get your "ego self" (shadows and compulsions) out of the way so that the true "you" (spiritual strengths) can emerge unfettered by any conspicuous feeling that you must censor your writing for fear that someone will criticize it. When you write for the spiritual autobiography, you write for yourself.

You are on a treasure hunt—searching for evidence in your life that God has always been there, and still is. These treasures are inside you, they are waiting to be unearthed, to come to the light of day in a time and a place when and where they can be more fully understood than in the past; you can consider them anew in the light of the majestic experience you have garnered to date.

No longer do they need be interpreted through your younger, less experienced eyes, but now seen in the fullness of the illuminating light of the Divine.

What to Write?

And what is it that you are to write about in your spiritual autobiography? You write about all the dimensions of your life, about "*the personal and the more-than-personal levels of your experience.*" (Dorff, page 17). You write about the good times and the times when you felt out-of-balance; the times of forward development and the times when you felt you slid backwards; you write about the mountain top experiences as well as the times when you slogged through the swamps of life.

Your writing holds the promise, the almost magical emergence of new revelations, the new insights that bubble to the top of your awareness as you delve deeper into the connections between life events that were formerly hidden from you, the associations among your many relationships that evaded your full perception "back then," and the fabulous interplay among and between all the arenas of your life.

Most of all, you write about your movement from one phase and stage of life to another, you identify the forces and powers that nudged you on, leading you down some roads and away from others. All of this, and so much more, becomes the subject of your personal inquiry into to yourself. Ultimately you begin to discern what Dorff calls the "*integrating rhythm*" (page 17) of your life, the beat of your own developmental drum that struck out a beat so steady and sure that it sounded the cadence for your journey of personal development and spiritual growth. When you begin seeing this deep unifying and undergirding theme running through your life, when you come to a keener understanding of it all, you quite naturally ask, "*...and who is the one beating the drum?*"

Writing your spiritual autobiography helps you awaken to the wonderful process of your life, rather than seeing only the results of your actions. So often our worldly culture myopically focuses only on what you produce, what you achieve, what you accomplish, as though the outcome was the only value. Such a perspective is denigrating to all, but especially to patients and chronic-illness "thrivers" (and their caregivers) who have seen a different vision of life.

Our current cultural vision seems to trivialize and even discount the illness time because it doesn't see anything productive about it. Such a perspective contorts the real purpose of life, the flowering of your true personality in the ongoing process of life. A product-centered world-view makes us blind to the magnificent wholeness of our day-to-day life, the fortifying "being" of life.

Writing your spiritual autobiography helps you discern the underlying unity in your life. You eventually come to the profound conclusion that there actually is now, and has always been, a thread of knowing that runs through everything in your life. This new understanding generates a silent solace of security for your illness time and beyond that lets you know that you are, and always have been, gently cradled in God's hands all along.

Your Life as a Spiritual Puzzle

Every day of your life you have written on your heart and mind. This grand data bank within you is a repository of all you have experienced: what you believe, how your see (and have seen) the world, what you have thought and are thinking, have felt and are feeling, a compilation of all your decisions, and an itemization of all that you have done. All this information is in a form that scientific researchers would call "raw"...the data is simply collected, lying there unorganized, un-assessed, and unusable. In such a state it has no particular meaning, you can gain no significant knowledge much less any instructive wisdom from it.

In order for wisdom to emerge from this mass of data, it must first be "processed," it must be analyzed, inspected, sorted, and arranged in ways that allow you to decipher the true meaning of what's there.

In scientific research language this evaluation process is called "crunching the data." When you apply the same evaluation notion to your "life data," it's called life review. Life review is the process where you intentionally sort through the reams of data stored in the memory banks of your mind, and ever so gradually bring each datum to light. Like working a crossword puzzle you pick up a piece, inspect it, and gain some idea of where it might "fit" into the larger scheme of your life. Unlike a crossword puzzle, where you are given a picture of the finished product, you have no such guide when trying to sort out the themes or schema of your life. You pick up a piece, only to lay it back down again without gaining the slightest notion of where it might belong. Again and again you handle the same piece, turning it, comparing it to other pieces, assessing possibilities, all the while trying to gain some understanding of an overall plan of meaning, or blueprint into which the piece does in fact fit somewhere.

During your illness transition time, much more than in former years, you search deeper for the meaning of your life to date, and the meaning of today as well. You long to grasp the overarching plan that your life has followed, even without your conscious realization. You yearn to see the life-map you have followed that gives you new perspective and a broader sense of the whole. You feel the angst of frustration from walking blindly on your quest for meaning trying to discover the unifying themes, the coordinating forces, the synthesizing patterns that can somehow be combined into a grand design, a picture of your life which makes you understandable.

Gradually the picture of our life emerges as the puzzle pieces find their rightful places in the whole. You come to fuller appreciation that your life is indeed following a grander design than you ever realized. Ultimately, as the pieces fall into place one by one, a masterful puzzle begins to take shape, and you come to understand that the Divine hand has guided your hand all along—creating the masterpiece that is your life.

For the grand design is of God. The plan you have been following belongs to God. Certainly you have deviated from the plan at times; undoubtedly you have strayed from the design. Your human, ego mind has created gaps or holes in your puzzle of life, places where you refused to let God lead you through difficult times. Yet God has even taken care of you here; it is in these gaps in your life puzzle, these apparent holes where God offers you divine forgiveness.

God's forgiveness, undeserved and uncontrolled, fills the gaps and holes of your life puzzle with healing grace. Through the eyes of forgiveness you no longer see the gaps and holes, because in their place you now see only the shimmering beauty of God's hand which serves as the cohesive "glue" holding all the surrounding pieces of your life puzzle together. God always fills your own human holes and ultimately makes you whole ... if you let God in!

Re-membering Your Past

"Some of the memories that come back to us we welcome wholeheartedly; others, we wish we had never re-membered. Welcome or not, all of these experiences are part of our lives. When we re-member them, it is often a sign that they now have something more to say to us."

(Francis Dorff, page 51)

Dorff uses the hyphen in re-membering to denote that the process of remembering is not simply bringing to mind events, etc. long past. Rather re-membering, according to Dorff, is to take these memories and fold them into your overall life perspective in new ways. The process of re-membering means that you use your memories to construct a new definition of self at this point...a new understanding of your past which is much more integrative and wholeness producing. He points out that your memories may in fact be dis-membered; fragmented, disjointed, and out-of-place. Writing about such memories allows us to consider them anew and to re-member them in a new context of your life, a context that has the benefit of 20/20 hindsight, a luxury that you didn't enjoy when the event, etc., first became a "member" of your memory.

This memory reconstruction process pays rich dividends for you in terms of generating peace and purpose in your life. When the event first occurred, its actual purpose in your life may have been clouded. Now in the new context of your current life that includes illness, with its enhanced insight, history, and wisdom, you may see its true meaning shining through the clouds of former years. You can see with renewed clarity, heightened understanding, and more highly-developed compassion.

What formerly seemed a wayward or unwanted act in the play of your life is now recognized as a true turning point that brought about wondrous growth that would otherwise be hidden. You can now see the delightful irony that the stone that was once rejected has now become the cornerstone. This image becomes a metaphor for so much of what you may have heretofore considered life tragedies or undesired clutter in your life, and which now has reemerged as the Phoenix and recognized as a pivotal point in your development.

Dorff reminds us all that memories, which return with heightened energy, are the ones that will become our best instructors. On a personal level, he suggests that a good way to begin meditative writing is to start a new page in your journal and simply let the memories flow back. Jot the memories down as they emerge in your mind without having to entertain them in any formal way. As others emerge you might be able to discern some pattern that can serve as a unifying standard for that particular phase of your life.

Self-Care Technique Eight

Finding Your Personality Voice

The Spiritual Strengths Healing Plan uses your personality as the basis for constructive change and eventually for healing. Your personality is perhaps your most valuable healing tool. What's important to realize is that each of your six premier spiritual strengths, and each of their corresponding shadows, and compulsions that flow from the strength have a "voice." I put the word "voice" in quotes to indicate that its voice is not an actual, audible voice but rather a silent nudge or invitation or directive that pushes you to use our personality in very different ways.

> *Each of your six premier spiritual strengths, each corresponding shadow, and each compulsion that flow from the strength has a unique "voice."*

For example, my personality believing function premier spiritual strength is HOPE; its shadow is <u>despair</u>, and its compulsion is <u>presumption</u>. Each of these three has a unique "voice" in my personality. I will act in very different ways depending upon which voice I choose to listen to. How I react to the symptoms of my illness (which may include emotional reactions like anger, sadness, abandonment, feeling sorry for myself, being misunderstood, irritability and the like; or they may include psychological reactions such as depression or anxiety; or they may include spiritual disturbances like feelings of abandonment, shame, guilt, fear of the unknown, distrust in God, and the like),

83

depends upon which of my three believing voices I choose to listen to.

The "voice of despair" tells me things like, 'It's hopeless.' Or 'You didn't deserve this.' Or 'Why me?' or 'Why can't anyone help me?' or 'Why doesn't anyone seem to care ...understand ...have an idea ...know what to do?' Such unconscious and semi-conscious mental concepts always make me feel worse, shatter my resolve, undermine my confidence, plant seeds of doubt and uncertainty, push me away from people, and generally block the healing power of my spiritual strengths of HOPE. The voice of the compulsion of "presumption" says things like: 'Why should you have to do anything to change your life, you didn't cause this illness?' or 'Look, you don't need to look for God; God will be kind you.'

Listening to Your Spiritual Strength Voices

What better way of creating a more fulfilling life than by mastering the art of turning inward toward your most inspired and ingenious self, the inner voice of your spiritual strengths. These voices are your guide of all guides to a life of centered healing and optimal functioning; genius, creativity, and a silent power emerge from your heart and mind the moment you do. The secret of tuning into these magnificent messages is having a heart filled with grace.

When your heart is opened wide, your spiritual strengths inner voices become strong and clear, and your most life- expanding messages saturate your personality. If your heart is filled with grace, it is almost impossible to stop your inner voices from speaking clearly and profoundly. Many great spiritual revelations and mental attributes are suddenly birthed from within you when your spiritual strengths voices become more audible than the many voices of your shadows and compulsions.

The saints among us, both past and present, were/are spiritually-healing masters who listened intently to their sublime inner voices more than the competing voices of shadows and compulsions. Those great beings that mastered this talent left their marks on history.

As your spiritual strengths voices grow in clarity and power, so will your healing when you listen. Learn to attune to that inspiring station from within. Listen as it guides you to new levels of creativity and healing. The voices of your spiritual strengths set you free on a new path of healing. Only the many shadow and compulsion voices of others, who live a life of mediocrity, can shut you down.

You can decide to expand your mind, heart, and soul through careful listening. Follow the steps below and commune with your wise inner guides. It will empower you, enlighten you, and catapult you to new heights of healing.

1. Stand relaxed with your hands loosely at your side.

2. Take a few deep breaths. Inhale and exhale through the nose slowly.

3. Tilt your head up a bit.

4. Turn your eyes up until you are looking forward and upward.

5. Close your eyelids and let them become relaxed.

6. Think about something or someone you are truly and deeply grateful for.

7. Keep thinking and thanking until you feel your heart has truly opened up and you have even experienced a tear of inspiration.

8. Upon attaining a grateful state, now ask your spiritual strengths inner voices for any guiding message.

9. When your heart is fully ready to receive the message, one will come.

10. Write this message down.

11. If your message is not become immediately clear, repeat steps 6 through 10 until it does.

Personality Pathways for Listening to Your Inner Voice

1. Identify Limiting Beliefs—Your Believing Function

We each carry a set of beliefs that we live by. Certain beliefs you hold consciously, while others are mainly unconscious. Beliefs develop out of past experiences and our interpretations of those experiences. Some of the conscious and unconscious beliefs that you develop limit your ability to grow and move forward in your life.

For example: One of your goals as a successful entrepreneur is to build an organization from scratch and hopefully make a lot of money. You discover that you have a belief - a limiting one - that it's wrong to make a lot of money. Until and unless you begin to alter your beliefs about money, it will be more difficult for you to achieve that financial success you desire.

Benefits: Learning to notice limiting beliefs allows you to become conscious of it, and then change it. Releasing a belief that limits you puts you back in the driver's seat of your life. You, rather than an antiquated/perhaps mistaken belief, make the choices that are right for you and allow you to fulfill your potential.

New Focus: You can increase your awareness of conflicting and potentially inhibiting beliefs and values by becoming more sensitive to inner clues such as a sudden feeling of interior hesitation, or a "ripple" of emotional confusion, or a shift in your affective state. Any such changes in your personality feeling function might be cues that offer you pause to consider where and how you may be fighting a belief or values clash. Take the time and consideration to unravel such clashes and move beyond them.

2. Connect with Your Body—Your Perceiving Function

Your body gives you a tremendous amount of useful information that you may not be conscious of. For example, when your mother-in-law visits, does your stomach tie up in knots? When your boss yells at you, do your shoulders turn into stone? When you feel passionate and alive, does your chest feel warm and open? When you ignore your body's message, you lose out on valuable information designed to let you know what works for you and what doesn't.

Benefits: For many people, fear manifests itself as tightness in the chest. This is valuable information, especially if you aren't aware that you are afraid. Your body alerts you to what makes you feel passionate and what doesn't. The body is a fount of wisdom designed to tell you when you're on the right path and when you aren't.

New Focus: Notice the messages your body is giving you right now. Try a self-massage to find areas in your back, neck, or shoulders that are tense or knotted. What other areas of your body feel tight? Which ones feel relaxed and loose? Use this information as another key to listening to your inner wisdom.

3. Notice Your Self-Saboteur—Your Thinking Function

Each of us has our very own special saboteur. The saboteur is the voice in your head that says, 'Y*ou are not good enough.*' '*Who do you think you are?*' '*If you take this new job, everyone will find out what a fraud you are.*' The saboteur's job is to "protect" you from taking risks and making changes.

Benefits: Learn to distinguish between your voice and the saboteur's mumbo-jumbo. Notice how the inner critic drives the choices and decisions you make.

New Focus: Simply notice the negative voices playing in your head. Notice the times when they crop up. Recognize that the voices aren't you and they aren't true. Learning to separate your own voice from that of the saboteur is a powerful and life-changing tool.

4. Check in with Your Heart—Your Feeling Function

Social conditioning teaches us to be logical and "use our heads." When you only use your head, your experience of yourself and the world is limited. You miss out on the vital information the rest of your personality feelings function, your heart, is constantly feeding you.

Benefits: The same neurological tissue found in the brain is found in the heart. The heart is a second "brain" and our emotional center. Listening to your head and your heart is crucial to good decision-making about your life, your business tasks, and your relationships.

New Focus: Put your hand over your heart and focus there - what is it telling you?

5. Listen to Your Intuition—Your Deciding Function

Intuition is knowing something without knowing exactly how you know it. Connect back to a time that you had a "gut feeling" about something - the job that you knew you shouldn't take, even though it looked good on paper or the relationship that just felt right for you. That's your intuition talking.

Benefits: Gut feelings are a wealth of information. Remember, your intuition is never wrong, although your interpretation of it may be incorrect. When your intuition calls to you, trust it.

Practice makes perfect when it comes to using your intuition effectively.

New Focus: The next time you need to make a decision, check in with your intuition. Experiment with trusting it. When you follow your intuition, what happens? When you hear it and disregard it, what's the outcome?

6. Listen to Your Behavior—Your Acting Function

Actions speak louder than words. "Your behavior never lies," is a foundation principle of psychology. Can you step back from your actions, look with new eyes on a particular behavior, and ask what it is "saying" to you about you?

Benefits: There is rich data to be mined when you take the time and interest to dig it out. Discerning the meaning of your actions, underneath the more obvious reason, informs you of your true motivation. When you ask yourself, *'Why did I say that to him yesterday, I really didn't mean what I said?'* or *'Why did I do that; I wasn't thinking?'* are good questions to ask because the answers provide you with an introspective treasure trove.

New Focus: Always look at what your behavior says. 'Why did I stop by at the ice cream store after my doctor visit?' or, 'What does it mean that I always forget my step-father's birthday?'

Self-Care Technique Nine

Healing Circles

Our ancestors met together in circles since the discovery of fire. Here in this place of warmth and security, sitting face to face, humans have long shared and learned, gained insight, and found inspiration. Now, many millennia later, the circle is engrained in our social and cultural DNA as a place for conversation, friendship, caring, and healing. We seek the belonging of the circle, the trust of the circle, the sustenance of the circle, and the power for good that emerges from the circle. The circle is compelling, and the circle is powerful.

We share common goals, learn a common language, and develop a deeper common sense around the circle—the circle is where we go to find our true selves. Words seem to take on heightened meaning and deeper significance around the circle...they somehow take on a sacred aura that feeds our souls. We connect with the deepest part of ourselves around the circle, and there find the presence of the Divine—we find God. We begin to contemplate the mystery that we are more than our bodies and even more than our minds—we are all connected by soul...to God!

You, the Circle, and Illness

I'm so taken by the work of Christina Baldwin and Ann Linea in their book The Circle Way: A Leader in Every Chair, (Barrett-Koehler Publishers, Inc., San Francisco, 2010, 218 pages) that I've devoted this section to some of their thinking as it relates to The Spiritual Strengths Healing Plan.

In the circle, you discover kindred souls who come together to find healing for the illness of illness. The circle presents a very special opportunity to re-kindle your own capabilities formerly unknown, untapped, and unused. When you experience "circle" you keep the flame of hope alive that your unique six spiritual strengths will carry you to a place of restoration...a place of sacred wholeness during your illness journey.

The circle is a learning ground for how to "be" with your illness, and still be well; its purpose is to jump-start all the silent and mighty mechanisms of healing within you into a sacred spin, the source of which is the same sacred power of spin that twirls everything in the universe—God. The healing circle informs you, it gives you new depth, it gives light so you can resolve conflicts, and a space for telling your story.

The circle lets all participants take a front row seat where all are welcome and all are equal. You form partnerships of healing in the circle, and forge deep personality connections. The circle inspires you, it gives lift to your center; indeed, the circle moves you away from the outer ranges of your shadows and compulsions and toward your sacred center of healing—your spiritual strengths.

New "miracles" of transformative healing grow in the rows and furrows of all the talking and listening in the circle. These "miracles" penetrate to your core, and with mysterious modes of action, they help you make the changes you need to allow healing to enter. Such "miracles" can only be activated by the sacred healing touch of the group. The circle gives you the special opportunity to connect with the hearts, minds, and souls of others who share your pain—in the process you discover healing.

The circle empowers you to take up your mat and walk free again regardless of what your illness may be doing to your body. The circle restores your sense of belonging at levels you've seldom experienced before. The circle gives you a place of rest and safety; it provides you a forum of new understanding, not in a rational sense, but of a soul sense. The circle can give your personality a garden where you can grow and bloom like never before...it fosters deep conversations of human awakening.

The language of the healing circle is the language of your spiritual strengths—God's language of virtue. This language lets you talk about your shadows and compulsions in an entirely new way, as though you're tapping into the Divine.

The power of story ignites the power of God's healing. You emerge from the circle refreshed and vitalized, ready to tackle whatever is necessary so you can tap into whatever is next in your illness healing journey. Mutual trust is healing, and motivating, and connecting, and revealing, and securing, and warming—the circle is the hidden garden of hope. It's a place to heal wounds and anticipate miracles.

The circle is confidential—absolutely; it's a place of curiosity and compassion; it's a place where you can ask for what you need, and offer what you can; and it's a place and a space where you can consider how all six functions of your personality operate. The circle teaches you to rearrange the best of you into a potent healing mix. The circle teaches you how to let go of that which holds you back and instructs you to harness the power that moves you forward.

A circle is more than a group. A group is an assemblage of people who have come to "get" something from one another—a circle is an admixture of sacred personalities who have come to "give" something to others. In the giving, they discover that they are ultimately gifted with so much more than they could possibly get otherwise.

Research

In his best-selling book Anti-Illness: A New Way of Life, David Servan-Schreiber, MD, PhD, relates the story of perhaps the most famous healing circle research. David Speigel, MD, a psychiatrist from Stanford University worked with the renowned psychiatrist Dr. Irvin Yalom, MD, offering support groups for women in treatment for breast illness. Because of their mutual philosophical orientations, the support groups soon morphed into true healing circles. Both Speigel and Yalom were convinced that:

"To be fully human, people ought to have as authentic a relationship as possible with others. They should know that in their deepest being they are intrinsically free to reconstruct and transform themselves, and they need to grant others this same powerful freedom."

(page 154, Anti-Illness)

To test their hypothesis, these doctors constructed a study where groups of eight to ten women in treatment for breast illness met once a week in a well-run support group. For a year the women met regularly before the group dissolved. At the end of the active study time, it was determined that the women had learned much as a result of the support group. They learned: *"...to confront their fears, to express their inner feelings, and to experience relationships more authentically; they were less subject to depression, anxiety, and even physical pain,"* as compared to women who acted as research "controls" and did not participate in such groups (page 155, op. cit.). Yet surprising and much more convincing findings awaited Drs. Speigel and Yalom.

Ten years after the research project, Dr. Speigel began contacting the women in the study, both those in the support groups and those who acted as control groups who did not attend any support group sessions. Only three of the 50 women in the support groups had expired, while not any of the 36 women who acted as controls, and did not participate in support groups, remained living.

This was incredible! What factors or forces might be responsible for this mammoth difference between the groups? What might be the powerful mode of action that caused such a dramatic result? How could meeting and expressing one's inner life, sharing one's personality, and lending a compassionate listening ear have any impact on physiology?

It seems that for all the reasons enumerated above, healing circles have immense positive impact on one's disease progress and healing. Further investigation determined that, "The more regularly a woman had attended (the group), the longer she had lived." (page 156).

This startling study is seen as a definitive link between psycho-social processes in a group and actual physical effects. The value of group participation is not a Band-Aid over the horrific invasion of illness; the therapeutic effects of the healing circle and group participation are real.

Spiritual Strengths Illness Care Healing Circles

Spiritual Strengths Illness Care Healing Circles can pay handsome dividends for participants. They—

1. Lend mutual support.

2. Provide practical education.

3. Tend to lessen guilt.

4. Teach techniques and skills necessary for living the most self-actualizing lifestyles possible.

5. Are resource centers for information dissemination.

6. Provide "affirmation of self" to each member.

Spiritual Strengths Illness Care Healing Circles accomplish this impressive list by affording group members an environment to—

1. Openly express their fears and expectations.

2. Feel trust in a climate of safety and acceptance.

3. Explore personal material with encouragement and support.

4. Partake in group process by inviting and even challenging members to become involved.

5. Become confident in their role as patient in their illness journey, or as caregiver.

6. Identify and express any conflict and/or controversy in their lives.

7. Overcome barriers of direct communication

Self-Care Technique Ten

Praying the Labyrinth

The labyrinth is an ancient tool known for its transformative and healing qualities. It dates back thousands of years and has appeared in diverse cultures across the globe from Crete to North America. A labyrinth is not a maze; there are no dead ends in a labyrinth like there are in mazes. Instead, a labyrinth mirrors our walk of faith and healing. Fr. Adrian Van Kaam so adroitly puts it, "Life is a mystery to be lived, not a problem to be solved."

Labyrinths are also different from mazes in that they have one well-defined path that leads you into the center and back out again. While there are many different labyrinth designs, the most popular design today is the one found in the floor of the cathedral in Chartes, France. The Chartres Labyrinth dates from the year 1220. It is forty feet in diameter, and is set with blue and white stones into the floor of the nave of the cathedral.

As you can see, the pattern consists of twelve rings that enclose a single path slowly leading one to the rosette in the center. The path makes twenty-eight loops, seven on the left side toward the center, leading to seven on the right side toward the center; these are then followed by seven on the left side toward the outside, and—finally—seven on the right side moving to the outside before terminating in a short straight path to the rosette.

The labyrinth is a tangible way to involve your body in your spiritual search. It is a pilgrimage, a journey of healing where so many come for blessing and hope of becoming whole. Walking the labyrinth (or finger walking it) comprises the three steps to spiritual development:

1. Purgation: detaching from the world.

2. Illumination: finding one's sacred center.

3. Unity: re-entering the world as a new person.

The Spiritual Strengths Healing Plan is uniquely suited for use in walking the labyrinth. The first part of the labyrinth walk, purgation, aligns with shedding our shadows...our unique vulnerabilities. The second stage, illumination, aligns with embracing our six spiritual strengths (identified for you in the Spiritual Strengths Healing Profile). The six petals or alcoves at the center of the Chartes labyrinth design offer a place of healing rest for each of the six spiritual strengths. The third stage of the labyrinth walk, unity, allows us to encounter our six compulsions, those proclivities that pull us off our spiritual journey and block our healing.

What is the Labyrinth?

A labyrinth symbolizes the journey of life, the journey of the soul. From a spiritual point of view, a journey is never "just" a passage in time and space, but also an expression of the desire for discovery and change. In folklore and religion, heroes and sages are often depicted as travelers (just think of such figures as Ulysses and Moses), venturing forth and restlessly seeking the light of truth, the promised land…"home."

Today, a journey is most often seen either as a nuisance or as a respite to "get away from it all." But a true journey is never escape—it involves initiation, growth, maturation, and movement that purifies you in the process. The archetypal journey is the pilgrimage, especially the pilgrimage to the "center," the Holy Land, which among Christians in the Middle Ages was considered the center of the world. A pilgrimage is always symbolized by hope: hope that the life journey of a human being goes through the peripheral to the central, through the accidental to the essential, and through death to life.

An authoritative voice on the labyrinth in America today is Reverend Dr. Lauren Artress. She is an Episcopal priest and minister for Special Ministries at Grace Cathedral in San Francisco and founder of Veriditas, the World-Wide Labyrinth Project, an organization that encourages the construction and use of labyrinths as tools for spiritual development and healing. Her book, Walking the Sacred Path (Riverhead Books, New York), is one of the best-known works on the history and process of the labyrinth.

Dr. Artress describes the labyrinth as a tool that allows you to explore your inner space and discover the sacred within. Walking the labyrinth becomes a pilgrimage into your interior. Pilgrimages have always been a part of the Christian experience. In early Christian times, Jerusalem was the favored pilgrimage destination. With the Crusades in the Middle Ages, however, travel to Jerusalem became a particularly dangerous undertaking and alternative pilgrimages to regional cathedrals, established as shrines, became common—evidence Chaucer's Canterbury Tales.

A description of the labyrinth from the Magnificat Retreat Center in Wichita, KS, describes that "...when one fully engages in the 'walk' of the labyrinth—one can experience a quieting of the mind, an opening of the heart, and a calling forth of a sense of wholeness, oneness, peace, and possibility."

Medieval pilgrims usually traveled many miles (most often on foot) to reach the shrine. Once there, they would end their pilgrimage by entering the church and begin walking (oftentimes on their knees) the labyrinth. This signaled that the pilgrim was now turning away from the world and inward toward God.

"Much of our spiritual seeking is driven by the desire to manifest our unique and individual gifts" (Artress, page 39). The labyrinth may illuminate ways you can use your unique spiritual strengths and point you toward your special spiritual tasks of healing. As a consequence, you may even uncover your personal inner passion, express your spiritual strengths, and pursue your new life purpose with vigor.

What is the Purpose of Walking the Labyrinth?

The labyrinth offers you an opportunity to listen to God in a very focused way, involving your whole being: body, mind, and soul. By walking the labyrinth, many people find insight into what they presently seem most concerned about. It can give clarity to your thinking and offer enhanced self-knowledge.

The labyrinth enlivens your personality so you can see, feel, and decide more accurately. It offers peace and tranquility by providing a place that points you beyond the world, a setting where you can feel as if you are approaching the outer edges of heaven. Using the labyrinth may help you find the strength for whatever changes may be necessary in your life; it offers you the stamina to carry on in the face of uncertain change brought on by illness or illness caregiving.

The labyrinth can guide you through your shadowy times, and give relief from the tribulations that you encounter in your life. Walking the labyrinth in faith can assist you in forming a more secure bond with the Spirit, and in so doing provide you the opportunity to exercise your True Self. It can become an avenue for walking back into your personal past, and a creative means for healing hurts that may still lurk in the shadows or your mind. It is a forum in which you can bring out your secrets, joys, misgivings, hurts, trials, hopes, disappointments, and find the peace, healing, and wholeness that you seek.

Healing and the Labyrinth

The motivation behind a pilgrimage nearly always involves some dimension of a desire for physical, psychological, or spiritual healing. Ramona Miller, in her article (*Presence*, May 1999) entitled "Sacred Place: An Opening to the Inner Journey," speaks of San Daminano, the Franciscan sanctuary outside of Assisi, Italy, which St. Francis restored, and where Saint Clare lived for more than forty years. She describes it as a place of healing where so many come for blessing with the hope of becoming whole. Pilgrims of today—whether visiting Lourdes or wailing the labyrinth—are no different from pilgrims of yesterday in that they seek healing and relief from struggles and suffering.

Even in our time of massive technological healthcare, a great hunger for healing exists. This hunger is perhaps as acute for psychological and spiritual healing as it is for physical cure. So many of us are damaged in some way... we carry burdens, wounds, and scars from what has occurred in our lives. Such burdens stifle our relationships and hamper our creativity, which we know to be two fundamental ingredients for healthy living and recuperation from disease. Artress says that walking the labyrinth, "...gives comfort to the aching heart and solace to a weary soul." (page 35).

Discovery of Self

Self-exploration—discovering the uniqueness in your inner depth—is a central, ongoing part of your lifelong spiritual journey. Whether consciously or not, you especially seek understanding of the unique Spiritual Strengths God has given you quite intentionally and individually. Both your body and your personality are distinct; no one else in the world possesses a body like yours, nor does anyone else have a personality identical to your own. Yet with this phenomenal diversity of body and mind, it is astounding to realize that you are even more different from all others spiritually as well. This unique spirituality is found in your Spiritual Strengths.

Central to your journey of faith during illness is the discovery of the uniqueness with which God has created you so that you can reflect your unique strengths ever more profoundly and show the love of God in everything that you are about. No one else can reflect God's love exactly the way you can. If you choose not to reflect any unique aspect of your personality, then that particular reflection will be missing from the world. You are commissioned to show love (John 13:34), to use your Spiritual Strengths and talents in God's service.

Artress sees the labyrinth as a place where you can "meet yourself" and come to better know your unique gifts (page 41). It can serve as a "spiritual classroom," where you can learn more about yourself and the cache of love that God has invested in you. Because the labyrinth invites you to the center of your being, you are better positioned in a more proximate mind-wet to receive what God has been trying to tell you all along; that you are loved unconditionally and that you are called to express God's love personally, creatively, unconditionally, and uniquely.

The Process of Walking the Labyrinth

As indicated by many people experienced in walking the labyrinth, this meditative walk can be viewed as a three-step process:

1. By moving toward the center, the walkers *release*, or let go of cares and concerns that distract them from focusing on the essence of life.

2. In the center, they pause, perhaps for several minutes, to receive *clarity* and *illumination*.

3. On the way out, the walkers may perceive a sense of *unity* that they bring back "out" into the world...a renewed vision and a refreshed spirit.

Artress explains these three stages in light of the classic spiritual journey.

1. Purgation. The first stage is entering into the labyrinth and making your way on the mystical path toward the center. This stage is where you "shed" your cares, worries, shadows, the things that upset you, the grudges that you may carry, etc. You allow the peaceful walking to purge you of anything that may be psychologically or spiritually toxic. This process of releasing, or letting go, frees you from the confines of the world; it unblocks the

free flow of energy within you, leaving you empty of your worldly troubles and—in quite peace—ready to receive.

2. Illumination. The second stage begins when you arrive at the center. Here you find the six petals of the labyrinth. The petals are said to be reminiscent of the petals of a rose. You can stop for a time at each petal where you can listen to "whatever might be there for you." Here, at the center, you are maximally receptive to receive, to soak up, and to take in. All this adds to greater clarity of mind and direction of purpose.

3. Union. In the third stage you reverse your steps and take the sacred path out and "back into the world." You have been nourished, received clarity, and given direction at the center. You emerge in confidence to meet the world renewed, more sure of whom you are, and empowered to bring God's light to the world. You emerge refreshed and rejuvenated, authentic and transparent, more real to yourself and to others.

Praying the Labyrinth in the tradition of The Spiritual Strengths Healing Plan

NOTE: Before you begin your walk, make sure you have your illness healing prayers from your book that align with your six spiritual strengths, shadows, and compulsions.

Step One

Have your six "shadow prayers" ready. As you step into the labyrinth, begin to recite your shadow prayers VERY SLOWLY, intentionally, reflectively, and thoughtfully. As you walk, imagine your shadows as thick metal-like plates that cover your entire body. "See" these metal plates begin to loosen and break apart. "See" them begin to slide right off you as you walk...these are your shadows falling away from you—leaving your "purged" of the tremendous weight and block they were for your previously. Continue in this manner until your reach the center of the labyrinth.

Step Two

When you reach the center move to the first alcove or pedal immediately to your right. In the first alcove, begin to read your believing spiritual strengths prayer VERY SLOWLY, intentionally, reflectively, and thoughtfully. Now move to the second alcove and recite your perceiving spiritual strength prayer in a like manner. Move through the third, fourth, fifth, and sixth alcoves reciting in each your thinking, feeling, deciding, and acting prayers respectively. As you recite your strength prayers, imagine that you are being showered by the healing grace (power and might) of each of your strengths. This healing grace is, of course, from God. Your job in the center is to be as receptive as you can so this grace impacts you with potent energy. You might even imagine this grace penetrating to the bodily sites of your illness and eradiating it.

Step Three

When you've finished in the center (and please know that you can take as much time as you like) you now begin your walk out of the labyrinth—retracing your entrance steps. On this journey out recite your six prayers for your compulsions VERY SLOWLY, intentionally, reflectively, and thoughtfully. As you walk imagine your compulsions as splints that were on your arms, your legs, and down your back, as well as a large head brace. These splints and brace were confining you terribly, restricting your movement, forcing you to walk and move only as they directed not as your "essential self" would want you to walk. You imagine these splints and brace simply falling away from you as you walk out of the labyrinth—freeing you to move smoothly and without impairment. Your True Self, not your ego self, is now taking the lead in your life. Again, on your exit journey you may recite your compulsion prayers as many times as you wish. As you emerge from praying the labyrinth you feel refreshed, free, flexible, and full of healing grace.

End Note

The ten self-care techniques are not ends in themselves; you don't practice them for their own sake, no...they are only the means to an end. The end toward which we stretch, the goal of our life now with illness, and beyond, is our faith: growing closer to God, finding healing, and living in the truth, beauty, and goodness of the Divine. These ten self-care techniques then are really spiritual disciplines: practices that help us grow closer to God, means to moving beyond living a mere physical existence, and opportunities to live as centered, balanced, and whole a life as we can, even in the face of illness.

Richard Foster, in his classic book, Celebration of Discipline, uses two metaphors to illustrate the purpose of spiritual disciplines: a field and a path.

A farmer is helpless to grow grain; all he can do is provide the right conditions for the growing of grain. He cultivates the ground, he plants the seed, he waters the plants, and only after all this work, can all the natural forces of the earth take over allowing the grain to take root and grow. This is the way it is with spiritual disciplines--they are a way of sowing to the Spirit.

Foster says, "Spiritual disciplines are a means of receiving God's grace. They allow us to place ourselves before God so he can transform us." He goes on to say that spiritual disciplines are like a narrow ridge with a sheer drop off on either side: there is the abyss of trust in works on one side and the abyss of faith without deeds on the other. On the ridge there is a path, the disciplines of the spiritual life. The path does not produce change; it only places you where the change can occur.

The task then is to cultivate your daily life into fertile ground in which God can bring growth and change. This is what the spiritual discipline of these ten self-care techniques is all about.

"Superficiality is the curse of our age…. The desperate need today is not for a greater number of intelligent people, or gifted people, but for deep people."

Richard Foster, Celebration of Discipline

"The spiritual life is first of all a life. It is not merely something to be known and studied, it is to be lived."

Thomas Merton, Thoughts in Solitude

http://www.watersedge.tv/disciplines_intro.htm

Made in the USA
Charleston, SC
08 March 2014